TESTS AND DRILLS

in

ENGLISH GRAMMAR

BOOK 1

(Revised Edition)

by

ROBERT J. DIXSON

REGENTS PUBLISHING COMPANY, INC.

Printed in the United States of America

ISBN 0-88345-159-X 4/85

How To Use This Book

The efficiency of this book will depend greatly upon the skill of the teacher who uses it. The book is planned very simply so that there is no real problem of organization of materials. Each lesson is arranged so that the teacher simply starts with the the first exercises of each lesson and proceeds through the remaining exercises. But the problem arises from the following: many teachers, and particularly the inexperienced teacher, consider the exercises to be simple and obvious, and they are unaware of the profound difficulty of these exercises to the non-English-speaking student. It is true that the exercises in themselves are not difficult to do. The theory behind the various grammar exercises is also not complex. English grammar, on the whole, is relatively simple, but the real teaching problem arises from the fact that the teacher must do much more than simply explain the exercises and repeat them once or twice with the students. *The students must be taught to use what they are studying.* They must be given sufficient practice and repetition so that everything they study is retained and made an active part of their everyday conversation. This is the basic problem.

It may be helpful to the teacher if she keeps the following in mind: learning to speak a foreign language is more or less a matter of acquiring a skill. It is a skill similar to the skill acquired in learning to type or to play the piano. It is therefore an ability which comes only with much practice and repetition. The theory involved is generally quite simple. One can understand the theory of typing, for example, after only a few minutes study of the typewriter keyboard, but to learn to type well requires months of patient practice. So it is with learning to speak and understand a foreign language. A student can understand the theory of most of the English grammar principles in this book after a few minutes study, but the ability to use these principles later in speaking English will require constant practice and repetition.

How can this practice and repetition be given within the limits of the usual grammar lesson without tiring or boring the student? This is the task of the teacher.

The following suggestions are offered: First, repeat all exercises several times. Each time go over the exercises a little faster, demanding from the students speed and accuracy. Also, don't try to cover too many exercises each day. Half a lesson is enough for the average class to cover in one day.

Second, ask students to close books and then have them do the same exercise orally—possibly several times. You will have to guide the students in this, and some exercises do not lend themselves to this treatment, but it can be done with the majority of the exercises.

Third, tell the class that you are now going to ask them some questions using the particular grammar principle involved.

Fourth (and this is very important), in the case of each grammar principle studied, have some simple oral drill of your own invention ready for use. These supplemental oral drills are very easy to develop. For example, if you are teaching negatives, it is very easy to say to the class, "Now I am going to give you a series of sentences orally and I want you to change them to negative form." You then give each student a simple sentence such as "I went to the movies last night," and he has to change it to negative form. If the class has already studied question form, you can also make the students put the same sentence into question form for further oral practice. You can next give them a list of negative sentences and make the students change them to positive form. Any such oral device will serve the purpose of giving the class additional practice in using what they are studying. On the elementary level the drills can be very simple. On the advanced level, with a little imagination, they can often be made quite interesting as well as practical. For example, in teaching the perfect form of the auxiliary *should (should have),* which is a rather difficult form for foreign students to use, I always proceeded as follows: First, I would run over the exercises several times until the students could do the exercises in the book perfectly. However, I knew from many years of experience in this work that there is a great difference between a student's being able to do the exercises in the book and being able to use the particular principle in speaking the language. Consequently, I then always explained to the class that I was going to give them a little additional oral drill so that they could practice using this form in their everyday conversation. I would then give them a series of statements which they were to consider as statements of error. They were to correct each of these statements using in their answers, first, *should have* in the negative form and, second, *should have* in the positive form. For example, I would say to the first student, "I waited for you last night on the corner of 33rd Street." He had to reply, "You *shouldn't have waited* for me on the corner of 33rd Street. You *should have waited* for me on the corner of 42nd Street." To the next student I would say, "I sent that letter by surface mail." He then had to answer, "You *shouldn't have sent* that letter by surface mail. You *should have sent* it airmail." To the third student I would make a similar statement, and thus I would pass all around the class until each student had had one or more practice exercises using *shouldn't have* and *should have.* I would also continue this drill for several days during the review section of later lessons. Naturally, after a week or so of this kind of practice, every student in the class understood the principle well and could use it in his everyday speech. Furthermore, the students always enjoyed such drills. They found them fun to do, and they felt that they were actually speaking the language rather than just learning grammar theory from a textbook.

Fifth, institute some regular system of review so that a good part of each lesson is devoted to the repetition of material of earlier lessons. In this way things learned today are not forgotten tomorrow. Instead, everything which has been studied is kept constantly fresh and active.

Sixth, for purposes of variety, occasionally dictate exercises to the class and make the students write as you dictate. They can fill in correct verb tenses, correct mistakes, change to negative or interrogative form, etc.

If the above suggestions are followed, I am sure that the teacher will find that her lessons will become much more effective. The teacher need not adopt all the points mentioned here; she can add other ideas which may fit her particular class situation better. But if she follows this oral approach and adheres less rigidly to the exercises in the book, she will find that her lessons will be more animated, her students will respond more eagerly to the task at hand. The students will also be able to make practical use of everything which they study, and thus the purpose of this book, as I have conceived it, will have been achieved.

For further conversational practice with the grammar principles of this book, the textbooks *Exercises in English Conversation,* Books 1 and 2, are strongly recommended as supplemental texts. The books have been written to accompany each other, and the exercises of this book parallel the exercises of the conversational books, lesson for lesson.

R. J. D.

CONTENTS

LESSON 1

1. Simple Negative and Question Form.

a) In English we form the negative of the verb *to be* by placing *not* directly after the verb.

He is a teacher.
He is *not* a teacher.
This is a book.
This is *not* a book.

b) We form questions with the verb *to be* by placing the subject after the verb.

He is a teacher.
Is he a teacher?
This is a book.
Is this a book?

EXERCISES

A. *Change to negative form:*

1. This is a pencil. (This is not a pencil.)
2. This is a book.
3. This is a pen.
4. This is a notebook.
5. This is a chair.
6. This is a window.
7. This is a door.
8. This is a room.
9. This is a table.
10. This is a telephone.*

B. *Change to question form:*

1. This is a book. (Is this a book?)
2. This is a pencil.
3. This is a pen.
4. This is a notebook.
5. This is a chair.
6. This is a window.
7. This is a door.

*The teacher can add to this basic vocabulary if she wishes by pointing to other objects at hand or in the room.

8. This is a room.
9. This is a table.
10. This is a telephone.*

C. *Fill in the blanks:*

1. This is a book.
   a. This is ...... (a) ......book.
   b. ....is a book.
   c. This is a................
   d. This.............a book.

2. This is a chair.
   a. ....is a chair.
   b. This is a................
   c. This..............a chair.
   d. This is.............chair.

3. This is a pencil.
   a. This.............a pencil.
   b. This is.............pencil.
   c. ....is a pencil.
   d. This is a................

4. This is a telephone.
   a. This is..........telephone.
   b. ....is a telephone.
   c. This..........a telephone.
   d. This is a................

D. *Give short answers to each of the following:*

1. Is this a book? (Yes, it is.)
2. Is this a pencil?
3. Is this a pen?
4. Is this a notebook?
5. Is this a chair?
6. Is this a window?
7. Is this a door?
8. Is this a room?*

E. *Give short negative answers to each of the following:*

1. Is this a book? (No, it isn't.)
2. Is this a pen?
3. Is this a notebook?
4. Is this a telephone?
5. Is this a chair?
6. Is this a room?
7. Is this a window?
8. Is this a door?*

---

*Here again the teacher, at her discretion, can add to this vocabulary, indicating other changes at hand or in the room.

LESSON 2

2. VERB *TO BE.*

a) The verb *to be* has the following forms in the present tense:

I am	we are
you are	you are
he, she, it is	they are

b) In everyday conversation, we generally use the following contracted forms with *to be:*

I'm	(I am)	we're	(we are)
you're	(you are)	you're	(you are)
he's	(he is)		
she's	(she is)	they're	(they are)
it's	(it is)		
there's		what's	

c) Rule 1a states that we form the negative of the verb *to be* by placing *not* directly after the verb. This is true for all three persons, singular and plural.

He's a teacher.
He's *not* a teacher.

You are a student.
You're *not* a student.

We're students.
We're *not* students.

In addition to the negative contractions *he's not, they're not,* etc., the following contractions of *to be* and *not* are commonly used:

I'm not	we aren't
you aren't	you aren't
he isn't	
she isn't	they aren't
it isn't	
there isn't	there aren't

d) Rule 1b states that we form questions with the verb *to be* by placing the subject after the verb. This is also true for all three persons, singular and plural.

He is a teacher.
Is he a teacher?

You are a student.
Are you a student?

3. SIMPLE PLURALS. We form the plural of nouns in English by adding *s* to the singular. There are some irregular plurals:

one pencil	two pencils
one book	two books
one man	two men
one woman	two women

EXERCISES

A. *Fill in the blanks with the correct form of the verb* TO BE:

1. I........(am)........a teacher.
2. John....................a teacher.
3. William....................a student.
4. This....................a book.
5. This....................not a pencil.
6. John and Mary....................students.
7. Two and three....................five.
8. We....................students.
9. John....................a man.
10. Mary....................a woman.
11. Three and two....................five.
12. I....................busy.
13. John....................busy.
14. Mary....................busy.
15. Mr. and Mrs. Smith....................busy.

B. *Change to negative form:*

1. I'm a teacher. (I'm not a teacher.)
2. This is a book.
3. We're students.
4. Two and three are six.
5. John's a teacher.
6. Mr. Smith's a student.
7. She's a man.
8. This is a good book.
9. They're students.
10. John and Mary are good students.

C. *Change to question form:*

1. She's a student. (Is she a student?)
2. We're good students.
3. John's busy.
4. Mr. Smith's a teacher.
5. Four and two are six.
6. Mary's a woman.
7. Mr. and Mrs. Smith are busy.
8. They're teachers.
9. John's a student.
10. I am busy.

D. *Give the plural of the following:*

1. One book, two .... (One book, two books.)
2. One table, three ....
3. One man, two ....
4. One chair, two ....
5. One teacher, two ....
6. One pencil, two ....
7. One woman, two ....
8. One room, two ....
9. One student, three ....
10. One window, five ....
11. One room, two ....
12. One notebook, three ....
13. One telephone, two ....
14. One pen, two ....

E. *Choose the correct word:*

1. I (am, is) a teacher. (I am a teacher.)
2. They (are, is) busy.
3. This (is, are) a book.
4. John and Mary (is, are) good students.
5. Five and three (am, are) eight.
6. We (is, are) students.
7. William (is, are) a student.
8. Mary (is, are) a woman.
9. John (is, are) not a teacher.
10. (Are, is) this a book?

11. They (am, are) not busy.
12. I (is, am) busy.

F. *Answer these questions:*

1. Is John a good student? (Yes, he is.)
2. Are you a student or a teacher?
3. Is this a notebook or a pencil?
4. Are you busy today?
5. Is Mary a good student or a bad student?
6. Are you a good student or a bad student?
7. Are John and Mary busy today?
8. Is George a good student or a bad student?
9. Is this a desk or a chair?
10. Is Mr. Smith a man or a woman?

LESSON 3

4. POSSESSIVE ADJECTIVES. The possessive adjectives in English (with their corresponding personal pronouns) are as follows:

I—*my*	we—*our*
you—*your*	you—*your*
he—*his*	they—*their*
she—*her*	

This is *my* book.
She's in *her* room.
He walks to *his* chair.

a) We form the possessive of most nouns in English by adding *'s*. Examples: *book's, Mary's, Mr. Smith's.*

This is *Mary's* book.
The *dog's* tail is very long.

b) We usually form the possessive of nouns that already end in *s* by adding an apostrophe only. Examples: *books', Charles', Mr. Ross'.*

The *students'* books are on their desks.
The *dogs'* tails are very long.

5. POSITION OF ADJECTIVES. An adjective in English always precedes the word it modifies. Adjectives also have only one form and do not change form when they modify singular or plural nouns or nouns of different gender.

This is a *good* book.
He is a *good* student.
They are *good* students.

6. VERB *TO HAVE*. The verb *to have* has the following present tense forms:

I have	we have
you have	you have
he, she, it has	they have

EXERCISES

A. *Fill in the blanks with the correct possessive adjective:*

1. I walk to.........(my).........chair.
2. John walks to .... chair.

3. You walk to .... chair.
4. Mr. Smith walks to .... desk.
5. Mary walks to .... seat.
6. Mrs. Smith walks to .... seat.
7. The boy walks to .... seat.
8. The girl walks to .... seat.
9. They walk to ....chairs.
10. The teacher writes with .... pen.
11. I write with .... pen.
12. The students write with .... pens.

B. *Change the words in italics to possessive form:*

1. This is the book of *John.* (This is *John's* book.)
2. This is the pen of *Helen.*
3. The desk of the *teacher* is new.
4. That's the home of my *teacher.*
5. The friend of my *sister* is very sick.
6. The office of *Mr. Smith* is very large.
7. This is the notebook of *William.*
8. He's the teacher of *Helen.*
9. He's also the teacher of *my friend.*
10. This is the room of *Mr. Smith.*

C. *Change to negative form:*

1. They're good students. (They're not good students.)
2. He's my teacher.
3. John and Mary are students.
4. He's a good teacher.
5. This is my pencil.
6. Mr. Smith's in his office.
7. We're teachers.
8. Seven minus three is two.
9. Five times two is nine.
10. This is their classroom.

D. *Change to question form:*

1. They're good students. (Are they good students?)
2. He is in his office.
3. She is a good student.
4. They're busy.

5. Six and one are seven.
6. This is his room.
7. This is their classroom.
8. This is John's office.
9. They're in the office.
10. He's busy.
11. She's busy.
12. She's in class.

E. *Choose the correct form:*

1. William (is, are) in his room. (William is in the room.)
2. (Is, are) this your book or my book?
3. This (is, are) his desk.
4. (Am, are) you a good student or a bad student?
5. I (am, are) busy.
6. My book (is, are) on the desk.
7. My books (is, are) on the desk.
8. They (are, is) in the office.
9. This (is, are) my seat.
10. We (are, am) busy today.
11. Mary (has, have) a new book.
12. They (have, has) no teacher today.

F. *Answer these questions:*

1. Is this your pen or my pen?
2. Is Mr. Smith your teacher or Mary's teacher?
3. Is this your seat or John's seat?
4. Is John a good student or a bad student?
5. Is he a tall boy or a short boy?
6. Are John and William in your English class now?
7. Is this my notebook or your notebook?
8. Is Mr. Smith a teacher or a student?
9. Is he a young man or an old man?
10. What is the plural form of *book*? Of *man*? Of *woman*?

LESSON 4

7. *THERE IS—THERE ARE.*

a) We seldom say in English, "A book is on the table." We say, instead, "*There's* a book on the table." Thus, the existence of any indefinite person or thing is usually introduced by *there's* or *there are.* (Compare the similar use of French *il y a* or the Spanish and Portuguese *hay.*) Note that we use *there's* with singular nouns; we use *there are* with plural nouns.

There's a book on the table.
There are two pencils on the desk.
There's a man in the room.

b) The negative form of *there's* and *there are* is obtained by placing *not* after the verb. The question form is obtained by placing *there* after the verb. (Note that in all questions in English a question mark is placed at the end of the sentence. No mark is placed before the sentence as in Spanish.)

There is a book on the table.
There isn't a book on the table.
There are two pencils on the desk.
Are there two pencils on the desk?

EXERCISES

A. *Choose the correct word:*

1. There (is, are) a book on the desk. (There is a book on the desk.)
2. There (is, are) three men in the room.
3. There (is, are) many people in the office.
4. There (is, are) flowers on the table.
5. There (is, are) a picture on the wall.
6. There (is, are) a desk in the room.
7. There (is, are) a notebook on the desk.
8. There (is, are) many students in our class.
9. There (is, are) many windows in our room.
10. There (is, are) a yellow pencil on the desk.

B. *Improve the form of the following sentences by introducing* THERE IS *or* THERE ARE:

1. A magazine is on the chair. (There is a magazine on the chair.)
2. Two men are in Mr. Smith's office.
3. Many trees are in the park.
4. Many people* are in the street.
5. Many students are in my English class.
6. A vase of flowers is on the table.
7. Two windows are in the room.
8. Only one door is in the room.
9. A dog is in the garden.
10. Many animals are in the park.

C. *Change to negative form:*

1. There is a book on the desk. (There isn't a book on the desk.)
2. There are many people in the room.
3. There is a blue book on the desk.
4. There is a table in the room.
5. There are two flowers on the table.
6. There are many students in our class.
7. There are many people in the office.
8. There is a picture on the wall.
9. There are three men in the room.
10. There are many windows in our room.

D. *Change to question form:*

1. There is a table in the room. (Is there a table in the room?)
2. There are two men in the office.
3. There is a chair in the room.
4. There is a notebook on the desk.
5. There are flowers on the table.
6. There are many windows in our room.
7. There are many students in our room.
8. There is a yellow pencil on the desk.

---

*Note that the word *people* is always plural in English.

9. There are two students in the room.
10. There is a man in the office.

E. *Change the following to questions and begin each question with* HOW MANY:

1. There are two tables in the room. (How many tables are there in the room?)
2. There are three men in the office.
3. There are four windows in the room.
4. There are six students in our class.
5. There are three pencils on the desk.
6. There are many books in our room.
7. There are six men in the office.
8. There are five chairs in the room.
9. There are three pictures on the wall.
10. There are two pens on the table.

F. *Complete the following in your own words:*

1. There is a ....
2. There are many ....
3. There is a ....
4. There are two ....
5. There is not a ....
6. Is there a ....?
7. Are there ....?
8. Are there many ....?
9. There are three ....
10. There is a ....

G. *Choose the correct form:*

1. John (is, are) a good student. (John is a good student.)
2. How many books (is, are) there on the desk?
3. (Is, are) this your book or my book?
4. There (is, are) two men in the office.
5. There (is, are) many students in the class.
6. I (is, am) busy today.
7. There (is, are) many people in the office.
8. There (is, are) a large desk in the room.
9. Three (womans, women) are in our class.
10. How many tables (there are, are there) in your room?

H. *Answer these questions:*

1. How many students are there in your English class?
2. How many boys are there in your class?
3. How many girls are there in your class?
4. How many windows are there in your classroom?
5. How many doors are there?
6. How many chairs are there?
7. Is there a map on the wall of your classroom?
8. Are there pictures on the walls of your classroom?
9. How many pictures are there?
10. Is there a calendar on the wall?

LESSON 5

8. PRESENT TENSE OF VERBS. Verbs in English have the following present tense forms:

I work	we work
you work	you work
he, she, it works	they work

This form of the present tense, the *simple present tense,* describes an action which goes on every day or in general.*

He always *comes* to school on the bus.
They *speak* English well.

9. IMPERATIVE FORM.

a) The imperative form in English, which is used to express a command or request, is the same as with the second person singular of the present tense of the verb. The subject (you) is understood but not expressed.

(You) Walk slowly.
Come back later.

b) The negative form of the imperative is obtained by placing *don't* before the second person of the verb.

Don't walk so slowly.
Don't come back later.

c) The imperative form is often softened in everyday conversation by the use of *please. Please* is placed either at the beginning or at the end of the sentence.

Please sit here.
Sit here, please.

Please don't walk so fast.
Don't walk so fast, please.

EXERCISES

A. *Supply the correct form of the verb:*

1. He........works........ (work) very fast.
2. I .... (study) very hard.

---

*The teacher should explain at this point that for an action which goes on *now* or *at the present time,* we use a different form of the present tense, namely, the present continuous tense—See Lesson 26.

3. She.................... (speak) very clearly.
4. They .... (walk) very slowly.
5. John .... (walk) very fast.
6. They .... (speak) English well.
7. This pen .... (work) well.
8. Helen and John .... (speak) English well.
9. He .... (like) meat.
10. They .... (drink) much coffee.
11. I.................... (drink) much tea.
12. I .... (like) to study English.

B. *Change each sentence so that it begins with* HE *instead of* I:

1. I like to study. (He likes to study.)
2. I am busy.
3. I have a book.
4. I work very much.
5. I am a student.
6. I walk very slowly.
7. I have a good teacher.
8. I speak English well.
9. I have a new hat.
10. I drink milk for dinner.
11. I like to study.
12. I have no money.

C. *Change each sentence so that it begins with* I *instead of* HE. *Change a second time to* THEY:

1. He speaks English well. (I speak English well. They speak English well.)
2. He comes to school on the bus.
3. He walks very fast.
4. He has many friends.
5. He likes to study English.
6. He drinks much tea.
7. He works very hard.
8. He writes many letters.

D. *Change to imperative form:*

1. You walk slowly. (Walk slowly.)

2. You drink milk.
3. You eat many eggs.
4. You speak slowly.
5. You have a cup of coffee.
6. You have bread and butter.
7. You eat slowly.
8. You drink slowly.
9. You study very much.
10. You speak English well.
11. You write very well.
12. You write slowly.

E. *Change the following imperative sentences to negative form:*

1. Speak slowly. (Don't speak slowly.)
2. Drink your milk.
3. Eat my bread and butter.
4. Eat fast.
5. Walk slowly.
6. Work very much.
7. Speak fast.
8. Drink much coffee.
9. Drink much tea.
10. Work slowly.
11. Write slowly.
12. Walk with John.

F. *Add* PLEASE *to each of the following imperative sentences. Read each sentence twice, once putting* PLEASE *at the beginning of the sentence and once putting* PLEASE *at the end of the sentence:*

1. Wait for John. (a. Please wait for John. b. Wait for John, please.)
2. Come back later.
3. Sit here.
4. Walk slowly.
5. Stay in line.
6. Don't mention it.
7. Don't tell Helen about it.
8. Speak more slowly.

9. Drink your tea.
10. Don't sit on this chair.
11. Don't wait here.

G. *Choose the correct form:*

1. What color (is, are) Mary's Hair? (What color is Mary's hair?)
2. John (speak, speaks) English well.
3. We (like, likes) New York.
4. (There, this) are my books.
5. Don't (walk, walks) slowly.
6. They (drink, drinks) much coffee.
7. He (have, has) a new hat.
8. There (is, are) two pens on the desk.
9. He (go, goes)* there every day.
10. They (has, have) many books.

*Most verbs ending in the letter *o (go, do)* form the third person singular by adding *es (goes, does)*. Verbs ending in an *s* sound *(s, sh, ch, x,* or *z)* also add *es* in the third person singular (wish, *wishes;* catch, *catches*). Verbs ending in *y*, preceded by a consonant, change the *y* to *i* and add *es* (study, *studies;* marry, *marries*).

LESSON 6

10. PAST TENSE—VERB *TO BE*.

a) The verb *to be* has the following past tense forms:

(Yesterday)

I was	we were
you were	you were
he, she, it was	they were

b) The negative form of the past tense of *to be* is obtained in the same way as the negative form of the present tense, by placing *not* after the verb.

He was a teacher.
He *wasn't* a teacher.
They were busy.
They *weren't* busy.

NOTE: The long form of *wasn't* is *was not.* The long form of *weren't* is *were not.*

c) The question form of the past tense of *to be* is also obtained in the same way as the question form of the present tense, by placing the subject after the verb.

He was a teacher.
Was he a teacher?
They were busy.
Were they busy?

11. PERSONAL PRONOUNS: OBJECTIVE CASE. The personal pronouns have the following forms in the objective case. (We use the objective case for all direct and indirect objects, objects of prepositions, etc.)

Singular		*Plural*	
(Nominative)	(Objective)	(Nominative)	(Objective)
I	me	we	us
you	you	you	you
he, she, it	him, her, it	they	them

He speaks to *me.*
I know *him.*
I understand *her* very well.
John likes *them* very much.

EXERCISES

A. *Change these sentences to past time:*

1. I am busy. (I was busy.)
2. John is a good student.
3. He is sick today.
4. He is at the movie.
5. William and Henry are at the movie.
6. They are good students.
7. Mary is sick today.
8. They are at the lesson.
9. Mr. Smith is in the office.
10. The book is on the desk.
11. There is a man in the room.
12. There are many students in our class.

B. *Fill in the correct past tense form of the verb* TO BE:

1. John .... (was) ....busy yesterday.
2. We .... at the movie last night.
3. There .... many students in our class yesterday.
4. I .... sick yesterday.
5. Mary .... also sick yesterday.
6. There .... two men in the office.
7. John .... not at the lesson yesterday.
8. He .... sick.
9. The books .... on the table.
10. John .... in Mr. Smith's office.
11. He .... in Chicago last week.
12. We .... with him at the movie.

C. *Change to negative form:*

1. John was in the office. (John was not in the office.)
2. We were at the movie last night.
3. Mary and John were with us at the movie.
4. There were many students in class today.
5. I was sick yesterday.
6. John was sick yesterday.
7. We were very busy yesterday.
8. He was here last night.
9. The book was on the desk.

10. The teacher was in the room.
11. They were in Chicago yesterday.
12. They were with us.

D. *Change to question form:*

1. We were at the lesson yesterday. (Were you at the lesson yesterday?)
2. John was sick yesterday.
3. The notebook was on the desk.
4. Mary was sick yesterday.
5. We were at the lesson yesterday.
6. They were very busy last week.
7. John was here last night.
8. There were many students at the lesson.
9. I was at the lesson.
10. The teacher was at the lesson.
11. Mary was at the lesson.
12. I was with her.

E. *Choose the correct form:*

1. John is with (I, me). (John is with me.)
2. I like (he, him) very much.
3. He studies with (us, we).
4. I know (she, her) very well.
5. I want to study with (they, them).
6. I understand (him, he) very well.
7. He speaks with (we, us) in English every day.
8. He studies in the same class with (me, I).
9. I go to school with (them, they).
10. I know (he, him) very well.

F. *Substitute the correct pronoun for the italicized word or words:*

1. John likes *Mary*. (John likes *her*.)
2. William studies *the book*.
3. She speaks with *John*.
4. I understand *the teacher* very well.
5. The teacher likes *Mary and William* very much.
6. He studies *his book* every day.
7. He goes with *Mary and me* to the lesson.

8. I like *this book* very much.
9. He goes with *John and William* to the university.
10. He speaks with *Helen* in English.
11. I know *William and John* very well.

G. *Choose the correct form:*

1. They (speak, speaks) English well. (They speak English well.)
2. We (was, were) at the lesson yesterday.
3. What color (is, are) his suit?
4. John (like, likes) New York very much.
5. He (work, works) very much.
6. (This, these) books are John's.
7. These pencils (is, are) also his.
8. There (is, are) a calendar on the wall.
9. (Has, have) you many friends?
10. How many windows (are, is) there in this room?
11. They (like, likes) their teacher.
12. We (was, were) at the lesson yesterday.

H. *Answer these questions:*

1. Where were you at ten o'clock last night?
2. Was Helen in class yesterday?
3. Were John and William in class?
4. Why was your brother not at the lesson yesterday?
5. Were there many students or few students absent yesterday?
6. What day was yesterday?
7. Was yesterday Tuesday?
8. Where were you last Saturday?
9. Who was with you at the movie last night?

LESSON 7

12. PAST TIME—REGULAR VERBS. We form the past tense of most verbs in English by adding *ed* to the simple form. All verbs which form their past tense in this way are known as *regular verbs.*

(to work)

I worked	we worked
you worked	you worked
he, she, it worked	they worked

13. INDEFINITE ARTICLES.

a) The indefinite article *a,* which is placed before all nouns of general or indefinite meaning, is not used before plural, when a certain number or quantity is indicated, by ing, no article is used.

I eat *a* sandwich every day.
I eat sandwiches every day.

However, the indefinite article is often replaced in the plural, when a certain number or quantity is indicated, by such words as *some, many, several.*

I have *a* book.
I have *some* books.
I have *many* books.
I have *several* books.

b) Note that in English the indefinite article is used before all predicate nouns which show the nationality or profession of the subject.

He is *a* Spaniard.
Mr. Smith is *a* teacher.

EXERCISES

A. *Change to past time:*

1. I walk into the room. (I walked into the room.)
2. John opens the window.
3. I look out of the window.
4. Mary opens her book.
5. I look at my notebook.
6. The teacher closes the window.

7. She likes this book.
8. John talks with the teacher.
9. We study English every day.
10. He walks to school every day.

B. *Fill in the blanks with the correct tense of the verb in parentheses (present or past tense):*

1. John .... walks .... (walk) to school every day.
2. John and I .... (walk) to school yesterday.
3. John .... (study) English with me yesterday.
4. John .... (study) with me every day.
5. I always .... (open) my book at the lesson.
6. I .... (open) my book at the lesson yesterday.
7. I .... (talk) with John last week.
8. John .... (talk) with the teacher every day in English.
9. I .... (study) my lesson last night.
10. I .... (study) English every day.

C. *Change from past to present tense:*

1. I opened the window. (I open the window.)
2. He walked to school.
3. She liked the book.
4. I talked with the teacher.
5. He studied* every day.
6. They walked to school.
7. She studied with me.
8. John closed the window.
9. I looked out of the window.
10. Mary looked out of the window.

D. *State in the past tense; also complete each sentence with words of your own choosing. In your answers make use of such expressions as* YESTERDAY, LAST NIGHT, LAST WEEK, LAST MONTH *to indicate past time:*

1. We (study) .... (We *studied* this same lesson *yesterday.*)

---

*When the present tense form of the verb ends in *y*, preceded by a consonant, the *y* is changed to *i* before adding *ed* in the past tense. (Examples: study, *studied;* marry, *married*)

2. John (open) ....
3. We (walk) ....
4. They (like) ....
5. Helen (close) ....
6. Mr. Smith (work) ....
7. They (talk) ....
8. John (study) ....
9. They (live) ....
10. She (marry) ....
11. They (arrive) ....
12. We (dance) ....

E. *Change the words in italics to plural form:*

1. A *table* has four legs. (*Tables* have four legs.)
2. A *chicken* is a bird.
3. A *carrot* is a vegetable.
4. A *cow* is a domestic animal.
5. A *lion* is a wild animal.
6. A *tiger* is also a wild animal.
7. A *cat* has a long tail.
8. A *dog* has a long nose.
9. A *baseball* is round.
10. A *football* is not round.
11. A *leaf* is green in color.
12. A *banana* is yellow in color.

F. *Change the italicized nouns in the following to plural form, and introduce* SOME, MANY, *or* SEVERAL *in place of the indefinite article:*

1. I have a *book.* (I have *several* books).
2. John has a *cigarette.*
3. There is a *man* in the office.
4. There was a *book* on the table.
5. We have a large *room.*
6. I write a *letter* every day.
7. Have you a *notebook?*
8. There is a *window* in our room.
9. I have a yellow *pencil.*
10. There is a new *student* in our class.

11. He has a new *notebook.*
12. There is a *letter* for you in the office.

G. *Choose the correct form:*

1. I (was, were) at the lesson yesterday. (I was at the lesson yesterday.)
2. John (has, have) many cigarettes.
3. (This, these) books belong to me.
4. He (like, likes) to smoke.
5. John (walks, walked) to school yesterday.
6. I talked with (he, him) about it.
7. How many windows (there are, are there) in your room?
8. I walked with (they, them) to school yesterday.
9. I write many (letter, letters).
10. There (is, are) several people in the office.
11. We (was, were) very busy yesterday.
12. They (speak, speaks) well.

LESSON 8

14. PAST TIME—IRREGULAR VERBS. Although most verbs in English form their past tense by adding *ed* to the simple form (see last lesson), there is a large group of common verbs which form their past tense in special, irregular ways. Such verbs are known as "irregular verbs." The past tense form of these verbs must be memorized.

(to see)

(Yesterday)	
I saw	we saw
you saw	you saw
he, she saw	they saw

(See Appendix for complete list of all irregular verbs, with their corresponding past tense forms.)

15. ARTICLES (Continued). The definite article *(the)*, which is placed before all nouns of particular or definite meaning, is used in the plural in the same way that it is used in the singular.

The book which I want is on the table.
The books which I want are on the table.

EXERCISES

A. *Change to past time:*

1. I sit at this desk. (I sat at this desk.)
2. John drinks much coffee.
3. I get up at eight o'clock every day.
4. I eat my lunch at one o'clock.
5. At two o'clock I begin to read my newspaper.
6. I buy many English books.
7. I often go to the library for books.
8. I come home at six o'clock every night.
9. I write many letters.
10. I read my English book every night.

B. *Change to past time:*

1. We talk with the teacher in English every day. (We talked with the teacher in English every day.)
2. John opens the window for the teacher.

3. We like this book.
4. We study English every day.
5. We walk to school every day.
6. I like to study English.
7. We walk to school together.
8. I often look out of the window.
9. He smokes many cigarettes.
10. They like to go to the movies.

C. *Fill in the proper past tense forms of the verbs in parentheses:*

1. I .... wrote .... (write) several letters last night.
2. John .... (talk) with Mr. Smith yesterday.
3. I .... (eat) my breakfast at seven o'clock.
4. I .... (buy) a new English book yesterday.
5. The teacher .... (close) the window.
6. I .... (walk) to school with John this morning.
7. I .... (go) to the library yesterday.
8. I .... (come) home very late last night.
9. We .... (begin) our lesson early.
10. We .... (read) the newspaper in class yesterday.
11. I .... (talk) with her about it.
12. He .... (buy) this book last summer.

D. *Change from past to present tense:*

1. He wrote a letter. (He writes a letter.)
2. I sat at this desk.
3. I got up early.
4. I ate my lunch.
5. He read his book.
6. I went to the library.
7. John bought a new book.
8. Mary began to study English at ten o'clock.
9. He drank much coffee.
10. I drank much milk.

E. *State in the past tense. Also complete each sentence with words of your own. In your answers make use of such expressions as* YESTERDAY, LAST NIGHT, LAST WEEK, LAST MONTH *to indicate past time:*

1. I (get) up .... (I *got up* early *yesterday morning.)*
2. We (eat) ....
3. He (buy) ....
4. He (write) ....
5. John (read) ....
6. The lesson (begin) ....
7. We all (go) ....
8. They (come) ....
9. We (have) ....
10. She (speak) ....
11. We (see) ....
12. She (bring) ....
13. They (sing) ....
14. He (drink) ....

F. *Change the italicized nouns from singular to plural; then make other changes when necessary:*

1. The *book* is on the table. (The books are on the table.)
2. I have the *cigarette.*
3. The *pencil* is on the desk.
4. The *student* is in the room.
5. The *teacher* is in the office.
6. I read the *newspaper* every day.
7. I read the *letter* from my friend.
8. The *window* is open.
9. The *door* is closed.
10. The *man* is in the office.
11. The *letter* is on the table.
12. The *room* is dark.

G. *Choose the correct word:*

1. Last night I (eat, ate) dinner at seven o'clock. (Last night I ate dinner at seven o'clock.)
2. They (was, were) busy yesterday.
3. They (speak, speaks) French well.
4. (Is, are) your books new?

5. He arrived (in, at) the lesson very late.
6. There (is, are) many people in the room.
7. How many English books (are there, there are)?
8. How many days (is, are) there in a week?
9. He (speak, speaks) English well.
10. (Are, were) you at home last night?
11. (Was, were) you at the lesson yesterday?
12. They (go, goes) to the movies every night.

LESSON 9

16. ARTICLES—(Continued).

a) The indefinite article *a* is used before all nouns of general or indefinite meaning beginning with a consonant (or consonant sound). The indefinite article *an* is used before all nouns of general or indefinite meaning beginning with a vowel (or vowel sound).

I have *a* glass of milk.
I have *an* apple.
He ate *an* egg.

b) Note that no article at all is used before nouns which stand for some indefinite quantity or quality (i.e., water, air, metal, honesty, truth, etc.). When such nouns are used to indicate some particular quality or quantity, then the definite article *the* is used.

Water is good for the health.
The water in this cup is not good.

Gold is an important metal.
The gold in this ring is expensive.

17. RELATIVE PRONOUNS—*WHO, WHICH.* We use the relative pronoun *who* when we refer to a person. We use the relative pronoun *which* when we refer to a thing.

The woman *who* came with him is his wife.
The man *who* spoke to me is Mr. Smith.

The books *which* I bought are English books.
The movie *which* I saw was good.

EXERCISES

A. *Fill in the blanks with* A *or* AN:

1. My teacher is .... (an) .... American.
2. Mr. Lopez is .... Spaniard.
3. John is .... student.
4. I ate .... apple.
5. Yesterday I bought .... sandwich.
6. I ate .... egg.
7. He is .... good student.
8. This is .... old book.

9. There is .... man in the office.
10. There is .... orange on the table.
11. Mr. Smith is .... Englishman.
12. This is .... English book.

B. *Put the correct indefinite article* (A *or* AN) *before these words:*

1. .... (a) .... pencil.
2. .... apple.
3. .... egg.
4. .... envelope.
5. .... orange.
6. .... hour.*
7. .... honest man.
8. .... house.
9. .... banana.
10. .... big banana.
11. .... exercise.
12. .... difficult exercise.
13. .... easy exercise.
14. .... university.**
15. .... big university.
16. .... used car.
17. .... old car.
18. .... new car.
19. .... young woman.
20. .... old woman.

C. *Supply the definite article* (THE) *where necessary in the following:*

1. .... fresh air is good for the health. (Fresh air is good for the health.)
2. .... air in this room is not good.
3. .... history is an interesting subject.
4. We studied .... history of France.
5. We must have .... good light in our classroom.
6. .... light in this room is not good.

---

*Since the letter *h* in the word *hour* is silent, the word begins with a vowel sound; therefore, we say "*an* hour," "*an* honest man," etc.

**The word *university*, although beginning with a vowel, is actually pronounced as though it began with the consonant sound *y* (as in *you*); therefore, we say "*a* university," "*a* used car," etc.

7. I always drink .... water with my meals.
8. .... water in this glass is dirty.
9. .... leather in these shoes is very good.
10. We get .... leather from the skins of animals.
11. We all need .... fresh air.
12. .... air in large cities is not very fresh.

D. *Fill in the blanks with* WHO *or* WHICH:

1. The girl .... (who) .... is with him is his sister.
2. The book .... I want is on the table.
3. The man .... came with me is my father.
4. Is this the pencil .... you bought?
5. Is that the bus .... we must take?
6. This is the chair on .... I sat.
7. John is the student .... speaks English well.
8. Was it William .... ate lunch with you?
9. The movie .... we saw was very good.
10. Is this the newspaper .... you read in class?
11. Are these the pencils .... you want?
12. Are these the boys .... study with you?

E. *Fill in the blanks with the correct prepositions:*

1. John walks .... the room. (John walks into the room.)
2. There are four chairs .... this room.
3. How many books are there .... the table?
4. The blackboard is .... the wall.
5. The boy drank a glass .... milk.
6. There is a pen .... the table.
7. I waited .... him .... the corner.
8. I want a cup .... coffee.
9. I look .... the window.
10. I always walk .... school.
11. I look .... my book at the lesson.
12. I write .... my notebook.

F. *Choose the correct form:*

1. John is (a, an) Spaniard. (John is a Spaniard.)
2. The books (which, who) I want are on the table.
3. The windows (is, are) open.
4. Yesterday I (got, get) up very early.

5. John (has, have) dinner at six o'clock every day.
6. (This, these) books belong to Helen.
7. Mr. Smith is (a, an) old man.
8. Yesterday (was, were) Sunday.
9. There (is, are) two men in the office.
10. He is (a, an) honest man.
11. (Was, were) they busy yesterday?
12. They (studies, study) English every day.

G. *Answer these questions:*

1. Are you an American or a Mexican? (I'm an American.)
2. Do you have a new English book or an old one?
3. Is that an orange or a lemon on the table?
4. Who's that man who's with Helen?
5. Was the movie last night a good one or a bad one?
6. Is Mr. Lopez an American or a Mexican?
7. Is fresh air good or bad for the health?
8. Is the air in this room fresh or stale?
9. Are the books which you bought English or French books?
10. Is this an English textbook or a French textbook?

LESSON 10

18. Negative and Question Form.

a) With the verb *to be* and with all auxiliary verbs such as *can, may, must,* etc., the negative form is obtained simply by placing the word *not* after these verbs.

John is a student.
John *isn't* a student.

He can speak Spanish.
He *can't* speak Spanish.

She must talk in the lesson.
She *mustn't* talk in the lesson.

b) With the verb *to be* and with all auxiliary verbs such as *can, may, must,* etc., the question form is obtained by placing these verbs before the subject.

John is a student.
Is John a student?

He can speak Spanish.
Can he speak Spanish?

She must talk in the lesson.
Must she talk in the lesson?

(Note that after all auxiliary verbs in English the infinitive form of the main verb is used and that this infinitive form always remains the same regardless of any changes in person, number, or tense of the auxiliary verb.)

19. Articles—(Continued). There is no article at all used in English before the names of cities, states, countries, streets, persons, etc.—when these names are used alone as proper nouns.

He lives on Fifth Avenue.
New York City is a very large city.
Mr. Smith is going to France, Italy, and China.

(*Exception:* However, with the names of rivers, seas, mountain chains, and countries, when such names have an adjective in them, the definite article is used. Examples: *the* Mississippi River, *the* Atlantic Ocean, *the* Rocky Mountains, *the* Soviet Union, *the* Dominican Republic, etc.)

EXERCISES

A. *Change to negative form:*

1. John is a good student. (John isn't a good student.)
2. He can speak French well.
3. He must do the work today.
4. They are busy today.
5. She can write English well.
6. There is a pencil on the desk.
7. Today is Wednesday.
8. Sunday is the second day of the week.
9. They must finish this exercise today.
10. The first month of the year is February.
11. There are six students in the class.
12. John can speak Italian.

B. *Change to question form:*

1. He is a very good student. (Is he a very good student?)
2. The students can speak well.
3. They can also speak Spanish well.
4. There are seven days in a week.
5. Sunday is the first day of the week.
6. Today is the eighth of January.
7. Monday is the last of the month.
8. Mr. Smith is a teacher of English.
9. The students in our group can study in the morning.
10. He can be here in an hour.
11. They are in the office.
12. There is a book on the desk.

C. *Change to positive form:*

1. He can't speak English. (He can speak English.)
2. There aren't seven days in a week.
3. Is he busy today?
4. Can he speak well?
5. The first month of the year isn't February.
6. Today isn't Tuesday.
7. Is John in class?
8. Must you go to class today?
9. She can't come to the lesson.
10. They aren't busy.

11. Can he speak Spanish?
12. He mustn't go there.

D. *Supply the definite article* (THE) *where necessary:*

1. We plan to spend our vacation in .... Mexico. (We plan to spend our vacation in Mexico.)
2. Later we want to visit .... Dominican Republic.
3. .... Hudson River lies west of .... New York City.
4. .... United States and .... Soviet Union are both large countries.
5. Some ships can cross .... Atlantic Ocean from .... France to .... United States in a few days.
6. You should take a trip sometime to .... West Indies.
7. .... Panama Canal joins .... Atlantic and Pacific Oceans.
8. The principal city of .... France is .... Paris.
9. He spent several weeks in .... Italy and several weeks in .... Spain.
10. We live on .... Madison Avenue.

E. *Fill in the blanks with the correct preposition:*

1. Monday is the first day .... (of) .... the week.
2. I saw John the day .... yesterday.
3. I want a cup .... coffee.
4. Mary came .... the room .... John.
5. I always have an egg .... breakfast.
6. I drink coffee .... a cup.
7. We walked .... school yesterday.
8. There are many students .... in our group.
9. I eat soup .... a spoon.
10. I always study .... the morning.
11. What did you have .... breakfast?
12. I eat breakfast .... half past eight.

F. *Choose the correct form:*

1. (Is, are) your friend an American? (Is your friend an American?)

2. (This, these) book is John's.
3. Yesterday I (get, got) up early.
4. Is this (a, an) new book or (a, an) old one?
5. There is (a, an) apple on the plate.
6. At ten o'clock yesterday I (begin, began) my lesson.
7. John (smoke, smokes) very much.
8. There (is, are) many pictures in the room.
9. I (was, were) at the lesson yesterday.
10. I spent (a, an) hour on my homework.
11. William sits near (we, us) at the lesson.

G. *Answer these questions. Give negative answers only:*

1. Is John a good student? (No, John isn't a good student.)
2. Can you speak English?
3. Can John and Mary speak English well?
4. Must I write my exercises in pencil?
5. Should Henry smoke so much?
6. Were you at school yesterday?
7. Were Helen and Ruth absent from school yesterday?
8. Are they good students.
9. Are you a good student?
10. Is today Sunday?
11. Are there many students in your class?
12. Is it ten o'clock yet?

LESSON 11

20. Negative and Question Form—(Continued).

a) In sentences where the verb *to be* or the auxiliaries *may, can, must,* etc., are not used, the negative form of the present tense is obtained by introducing the special auxiliaries *do* and *does*. *Do* is used for all persons singular and plural except the third person singular. *Does* is used for the third person singular. The word *not* then follows these auxiliaries.

We study English.
We *don't* study English.

They speak well.
They *don't* speak well.

He lives on Fifth Avenue.
He *doesn't* live on Fifth Avenue.

The long form of *don't* is *do not;* the long form of *doesn't* is *does not*. The contractions are generally used both in conversation and in writing.

b) The question form of such sentences as those described above (where the verb *to be* or the auxiliaries *can, may, must,* etc., are not used) is also obtained by use of special auxiliaries *do* and *does*. These auxiliaries are placed before the subject.

We study English.
Do we study English?

They speak well.
Do they speak well?

He lives on Fifth Avenue.
Does he live on Fifth Avenue?

c) We obtain the negative and question forms of *to have* in the same way that we obtain the negative and question forms of other verbs—namely, by the use of the auxiliary verbs *do* and *does*.

Question

do I have?	do we have?
do you have?	do you have?
does he have?	do they have?

Negative

I don't have	we don't have
you don't have	you don't have
he doesn't have	they don't have

d) When question words such as *Where, When, Why, How much, What time,* etc., are used, the order of the words remains the same as in simple question form; i.e., the auxiliary verb is placed before the subject.

He *can* come later.
When *can* he come?

They study English.
What language *do* they study?

He lives on Fifth Avenue.
Where *does* he live?

EXERCISES

A. *Change to negative form:*

1. They study English every day. (They don't study English every day.)
2. John studies English with us.
3. They walk to work.
4. She lives in the United States.
5. He comes here every day.
6. They always eat in the cafeteria.
7. He goes home early every day.
8. He often talks in English with the teacher.
9. They read the newspaper in class.
10. I like to look out of the window.
11. John walks to work.
12. They speak French.

B. *Change to negative form:*

1. I have a book. (I don't have a book.)
2. They have many books.
3. John has a new teacher.
4. I have two pens.
5. They have a new room.
6. He has a large office.

7. Mary and John have new hats.
8. He has a good notebook.
9. Mary and I have a good teacher.
10. Mr. Smith has many students.
11. She has a new hat.
12. They have many friends.

C. *Change to question form:*

1. They come here every morning. (Do they come here every morning?)
2. He comes here at two o'clock.
3. They always walk to work.
4. John drinks much tea.
5. They like to study English.
6. John speaks French well.
7. He often goes to the movie.
8. I like to talk with him.
9. He eats in the cafeteria every day.
10. He gets up early every morning.
11. They live in New York.
12. He likes Chicago.

D. *Change to question form:*

1. John has a new suit. (Does John have a new suit?)
2. They have a new room.
3. He has many friends.
4. You have a new notebook.
5. Mary and John have new hats.
6. Mr. Smith has many students.
7. You have a new teacher.
8. He has a red pencil.
9. Mary has a blue pen.
10. Mr. Smith has a small office.

E. *Change to question form and begin each question with the question word in parentheses:*

1. He lives on Madison Avenue. (Where) (*Where* does he live?)
2. She eats lunch in the cafeteria. (Where)
3. Our lesson begins at nine o'clock. (What time)

4. They buy many books in that store. (What)
5. He visits us every Friday night. (When)
6. He speaks French. (What language)
7. He eats in that restaurant because the food is good there. (Why)
8. She speaks English very well. (How well)
9. He comes to school by bus. (How)
10. He goes to the movie every night. (How often)
11. The train arrives at five o'clock. (What time)
12. I meet him on the corner every morning. (Where)
13. They read *The New York Times* in class. (Which newspaper)
14. He speaks English with all his friends because he needs the practice. (Why)

F. *Change to question form. Begin each question with some question word of your own such as* WHY, WHEN, WHERE, WHAT TIME, HOW, HOW MUCH, HOW MANY:

1. She lives in Venezuela. (Where does she live?)
2. He visits us every weekend.
3. They go to school by bus.
4. He goes to the park in order to see the animals.
5. The plane arrives at noon.
6. They always meet him in the airport.
7. They spend much time on their English.
8. He reads many English books and magazines.
9. He goes to the hospital every day to see his friend.
10. He gets up at six o'clock every morning.

G. *Change to positive form:*

1. They don't speak well. (They speak well.)
2. John doesn't like her.
3. Do they read well?
4. She doesn't write many letters.
5. Does John like New York?
6. They don't study English every day.
7. Do they always eat here?
8. He doesn't walk to work.
9. Do they speak French?
10. Does Mary speak French?

11. Mary doesn't speak French.
12. Does she read English well?

H. *Choose the correct form:*

1. There (is, are) seven days in a week. (There are seven days in a week.)
2. John usually (get, gets) up early.
3. John (has, have) many friends.
4. Yesterday they (go, went) to the park.
5. How many English books (you have, have you?)
6. We (was, were) very busy yesterday.
7. (Is, are) there eight days in a week?
8. We always drink coffee (in, from) a cup.
9. Is John (a, an) American or (a, an) Spaniard?
10. I (get, gets) up at eight o'clock every morning.
11. I (eat, ate) lunch early yesterday.
12. I (come, came) home late last night.

I. *Answer these questions. Give negative answers only:*

1. Do you live in Chicago? (No, I don't live in Chicago.)
2. Does John live in Chicago?
3. Does Helen speak English well?
4. Do we always arrive at the lesson on time?
5. Does Friday come before Thursday?
6. Does the month of February come before the month of January?
7. Do you get up early every morning?
8. Do you always prepare your lessons well?
9. Does John get good marks on his examinations?
10. Do you drink much coffee?
11. Do you live near John?

LESSON 12

21. USE OF *SAY - TELL*. The verbs *say* and *tell* differ in the way they are used. *Say* is always used when the words of a speaker are given directly.

John said, "I am busy today."
Mary said, "He is a good student."

When the words of a speaker are given indirectly, both *say* and *tell* may be used. *Say*, however, can be used only when the person to whom the words are spoken is not mentioned. When the person is mentioned (i.e., when there is an indirect object) *tell* is used.

John said that he was busy.
John told *me* that he was busy.

Mary said that he was a good student.
Mary told *us* that he was a good student.

22. ARTICLES—(Continued). Under Rule 19 it was stated that no article is used before the names of cities, states, countries, etc.—when these are used alone as proper nouns. However, when these names are not used alone but are used as adjectives to modify other nouns, then an article is used.

Mexico has a warm climate.
The Mexican climate is warm.

New York is a large city.
The New York subways go very fast.

EXERCISES

A. *Fill in the blanks with* SAY *or* TELL:

1. John .... (says) .... that he is very busy today.
2. Yesterday I .... my teacher that I liked my lessons.
3. John .... yesterday, "I am a good student."
4. Yesterday John .... me all about his country.
5. He .... that English is very difficult for him.
6. Mary .... that her mother is sick.
7. The teacher .... that he likes the spring.
8. Mary .... that she doesn't like hot weather.

9. Can you .... me where the office is?
10. Please .... John that I can't meet him today.
11. Yesterday John .... me that he was sick.
12. Please .... Mary that I can't see her tomorrow.

B. *Change* SAY *to* TELL. *Then make whatever other changes are necessary:*

1. He said that he was sick. (He told me that he was sick.)
2. Mr. Smith said that he was too busy to go with us.
3. John said that he could* not go with us to the park.
4. She said that she could speak French.
5. William said that his brother was sick.
6. Helen said that she liked to swim.
7. I said that I was too tired to go with them.
8. The teacher said that George was a good student.

C. *Change* TELL *to* SAY. *Then make whatever other changes are necessary:*

1. He told me that he could speak French well. (He said that he could speak French well.)
2. I told him that I liked to swim.
3. The teacher told us that our compositions were very good.
4. Mr. Smith told us that he knew how to play tennis.
5. I told him that I knew how to play too.
6. John told us that his father was an engineer.
7. I told Helen that I couldn't wait for her.
8. Mary told us that her mother was ill.

D. *Fill in the blanks with the correct articles where needed:*

1. He lives in .... Mexico. (He lives in Mexico.)
2. .... Mexican climate is warm.
3. We walked along .... Broadway.
4. .... Broadway buses are slow.
5. .... New York subways are very fast.
6. .... New York is a large city.
7. .... England is a small country.
8. .... English language is easy.
9. .... Europe is a large continent.

**Could* is the past tense form of *can*.

10. .... World War I began in 1914.
11. .... Broadway is a long street.
12. .... Broadway theaters are very good.

E. *Fill in the blanks with the correct preposition:*

1. There are four seasons .... (in) .... a year.
2. Spring is the first season .... the year.
3. Spring begins .... March 21.
4. It is often hot .... summer.
5. .... whom did you speak?
6. Do you go .... school every day?
7. What are the days .... the week?
8. He is a teacher .... Spanish.
9. We have our lesson .... the morning.
10. .... World War I began in 1914.
11. He told me .... his trip.
12. .... Broadway theaters are very good.

F. *Choose the correct form:*

1. There are four seasons .... (in) .... a year.
   come before summer?)
2. What time does John usually (get, gets) up?
3. Spring begins .... March 21.
4. John (has, have) a new suit.
5. There (is, are) many people in our class.
6. William is (a, an) Frenchman.
7. John is (a, an) Englishman.
8. What time (do, does) your lesson begin?
9. Whose books (is, are) these?
10. Is (this, these) your book?
11. We (have, has) much work to do today.
12. John (said, told) me he was busy yesterday.

G. *Answer the questions:*

1. Who said that William was sick today? (The teacher said that William was sick today.)
2. Who told you that William was sick today?
3. Who said that Helen was absent from class this morning?
4. Who told you that Helen was absent from class this morning?

5. Can you tell me what time it is?
6. Can you tell me where John lives?
7. Does Mexico have a warm climate or a cold climate?
8. Is the Mexican climate warm or cold?
9. Is English easy or difficult to learn?
10. Is the English language easy or difficult to learn?
11. Is New York City a large city or a small city?
12. Are the New York City subways fast or slow?

LESSON 13

23. NEGATIVE AND QUESTION FORM—PAST TENSE.

a) With the past tense forms of the verb *to be* (was, were) and with the past tense forms of all auxiliary verbs such as, *can, may,* etc. (could, might, etc.), the negative form is obtained by placing *not* directly after these verbs.

I was busy yesterday.
I *wasn't* busy yesterday.

I could meet you.
I *couldn't* meet you.

b) With the past tense forms of the verb *to be* (was, were) and with the past tense forms of all auxiliary verbs such as *can, may,* etc. (could, might, etc.) the question form is obtained by placing these verbs before the subject.

John was here yesterday.
Was John here yesterday?

He could meet you.
Could he meet you?

24. EXCLAMATORY FORM. We express exclamations in English by use of *What* followed by the the appropriate noun*, as shown in the following examples:

What a large tree!
What a pretty girl!

Note that, in accordance with the correct use of articles, no article is used in such exclamations before plural nouns or nouns of indefinite quantity or quality (see Rules 13a and 16b).

What large trees!
What strength he has!

EXERCISES

A. *Change to negative form:*

1. John was busy yesterday. (John wasn't busy yesterday.)
2. John is busy today.

---

*Exclamatory form with adjectives and adverbs is expressed with *How*. (*How* hot it is today! *How* well she speaks English!)

3. Mary can come to the lesson today.
4. Mary could come to the lesson yesterday.
5. You may smoke here.
6. John was at the lesson last night.
7. We were at the movie yesterday.
8. I may be late for the lesson.
9. John must speak Spanish in the lesson.
10. The books were on the table.
11. I can see you tomorrow.
12. He could do it well.

B. *Change to question form:*

1. Mary was here at two o'clock. (Was Mary here at two o'clock?)
2. Mary is here now.
3. John can see you tomorrow.
4. John could speak well last year.
5. We may sit here.
6. We must write in ink.
7. The students were in the office.
8. Mr. Smith is in Washington today.
9. He was also in Washington yesterday.
10. She can speak English well.
11. She could study in the evening last year.
12. There were many pictures on the wall.

C. *Change to question form. Begin each sentence with some question word like* WHEN, WHERE, WHY, WHAT TIME:

1. Mary was at the lesson this morning. (Where was Mary this morning?)
2. John can meet us at two o'clock.
3. There were three books on the table.
4. You may smoke in this room.
5. She could speak English well last year.
6. John was busy yesterday.
7. We may study in this room.
8. You must be here at three o'clock.
9. There are twelve students in our class.
10. There were many students in class yesterday.
11. We can study in this room.
12. We must be at the lesson at two o'clock.

D. *Supply* WHAT *or* WHAT A *in the following exclamatory sentences:*

1. .... good idea! (What a good idea!)
2. .... beautiful day!
3. .... pretty eyes she has!
4. .... strange thing to say!
5. .... easy exercise!
6. .... difficult lesson!
7. .... funny name to give a dog!
8. .... good coffee!
9. .... happy child!
10. .... happy children!
11. .... beautiful music!
12. .... large room!
13. .... foolish mistake!
14. .... hot day!
15. .... beautiful weather!

E. *Complete the following exclamatory sentences in your own words:*

1. What a beautiful .... ! (What a beautiful day!)
2. What a large .... !
3. What a pretty .... !
4. What a hot .... !
5. What an easy .... !
6. What a difficult .... !
7. What good .... !
8. What a good .... !
9. What a large .... !
10. What strange .... !
11. What a happy .... !
12. What happy .... !

F. *Fill in the blanks with the correct preposition:*

1. Were you .... (at) .... the lesson yesterday?
2. What kind .... fruit do you like?
3. What are the four seasons .... the year?
4. I like to look .... the window.
5. Does John go .... school .... Sunday?
6. January comes .... February.

7. March comes .... February.
8. There are four seasons .... a year.
9. We eat soup .... a spoon.
10. We eat soup .... a bowl.
11. I like to walk .... school.
12. I saw him .... two o'clock .... the afternoon.

G. *Choose the correct form:*

1. There (is, are) two men in the office. (There are two men in the office.)
2. I always eat (a, an) egg for breakfast.
3. They (was, were) not in class yesterday.
4. I (can, could) not be at the lesson yesterday.
5. I (eat, ate) lunch with John yesterday.
6. Is this the book (who, which) you want?
7. Mr. Smith is the one (who, which) wants to see you.
8. Where (do, does) John live?
9. John (said, told) me that he could not come to the lesson.
10. How many books (are, is) here.
11. Henry likes to (speak, speaks) English.
12. Do John and Mary always (walk, walks) to school?

LESSON 14

25. Negative and Question Form—Past Tense.

a) In past time sentences, where the verb *to be* or the auxiliaries *can, may,* etc., are not used in their past form, the negative form is obtained by use of the special auxiliary verb *did.* (Compare with use of *do* and *does* in the present tense; see Rule 20.) The word *not* then follows this auxiliary.

He studied with us yesterday.
He *didn't* study with us yesterday.

They saw Mr. Smith last night.
They *didn't* see Mr. Smith last night.

The long form of *didn't* is *did not.*

b) In past time, sentences where the verb *to be* or the auxiliaries *can, may,* etc., are not used in their past form, the question form is also obtained by use of the special auxiliary verb *did. Did,* as is customary with all auxiliary verbs, is placed before the subject to form the question.

He studied with us yesterday.
Did he study with us yesterday?

They saw Mr. Smith last night.
Did they see Mr. Smith last night?

c) In all questions in the past tense, as in the present tense, if some question word like *why, where, when, what time,* etc., is used, the regular question form is still retained; i.e., the auxiliary verb is placed before the subject.

He studied with us yesterday.
Did he study with us yesterday?
When did he study with us?
Why did he study with us yesterday?

He was here at two o'clock.
Was he here at two o'clock?
What time was he here?
Why was he here at two o'clock?

EXERCISES

A. *Change to negative form:*

1. I walked to school yesterday. (I didn't walk to school yesterday.)

2. John ate his lunch in the cafeteria.
3. We studied English at home last night.
4. Our lesson began at nine o'clock.
5. I went home at six o'clock.
6. We read the newspaper in class yesterday.
7. I came to school early this morning.
8. I liked the movie last night.
9. He spoke to me about it.
10. I drank much coffee yesterday.
11. I got up early this morning.
12. Mr. Smith said that he was busy.

B. *Change to question form:*

1. John ate lunch with me yesterday. (Did John eat lunch with you yesterday?)
2. Later we went to the movie.
3. We liked the movie very much.
4. Our lesson began on time this morning.
5. I came to school by bus this morning.
6. I went home last night by bus.
7. I drank milk with my lunch.
8. He studied English in South America last year.
9. I saw John yesterday.
10. We read our compositions in class.
11. Mr. Smith went to Washington yesterday.
12. I heard what he said.

C. *Change to question form. Begin each question with the question word in parentheses:*

1. He left for school at ten o'clock. (What time) *(What time did he leave for school?)*
2. I saw him this morning. (When)
3. I saw him in the cafeteria this morning. (Where)
4. He bought this book on Fifth Avenue. (Where)
5. He paid two dollars for it. (How much)
6. I slept ten hours last night. (How many hours)
7. We ate lunch in the cafeteria. (Where)
8. They came to school by bus. (How)
9. They lived in France for ten years. (How long)
10. I got up at six o'clock this morning. (What time)

11. He left because he was angry. (Why)
12. He promised to meet me on the corner. (Where)
13. He learned English before he came here. (When)
14. He said that he was busy. (What)

D. *Change to question form. Begin each question with some question word of your own such as* WHEN, WHERE, WHY, WHAT TIME, HOW MUCH:

1. He left for New York on Wednesday. (When did he leave for New York?)
2. He went by plane.
3. We ate lunch in the restaurant on the corner.
4. John's father just bought a new Chevrolet.
5. He sold his old car for eight hundred dollars.
6. I got up at six o'clock this morning.
7. John went to the hospital to see his friend.
8. He stayed with his friend for two hours.
9. They operated on his friend for appendicitis yesterday.
10. I slept more than ten hours last night.
11. Helen put all her books on her desk.
12. The teacher told her to put them inside the desk.

E. *Change to positive form:*

1. He didn't eat with me. (He ate with me.)
2. Did Mary see John yesterday?
3. We didn't like the movie.
4. Did he come early?
5. He didn't speak about it.
6. I didn't drink tea.
7. He didn't go home with us.
8. Did they come with you?
9. Did you get up early?
10. Did he read the newspaper?
11. He didn't tell us about it.
12. Did you hear what he said?

F. *Choose the correct form:*

1. (Did, does) John eat lunch with you yesterday? (Did John eat lunch with you yesterday?)
2. (Did, does) John eat lunch with you every day?

3. What time (do, did) you get up yesterday?
4. What time (do, did) you get up every day?
5. What time (was, were) John here yesterday?
6. Men (see, sees) with their eyes.
7. This is the man (who, which) wants to see you.
8. Do you want (a, an) apple or (a, an) banana?
9. Yesterday John (put, puts) his book on his desk.
10. John (get, gets) up every morning at eight o'clock.
11. (This, these) books are new.
12. Does a man (walk, walks) with his hands or with his feet?

G. *Answer these questions. Give negative answers only:*

1. Did you arrive at school on time this morning? (No, I didn't arrive at school on time yesterday.)
2. Did John walk to school with you?
3. Did you sleep well last night?
4. Do you read the newspapers every morning?
5. Did you read the newspaper this morning?
6. Do you prepare your homework every night?
7. Did you prepare your homework last night?
8. Do you eat lunch in the cafeteria every day?
9. Did you eat lunch in the cafeteria yesterday?
10. Were you absent from school yesterday?

LESSON 15

26. NEGATIVE QUESTIONS. Negative questions in all tenses are formed like simple questions; that is, the auxiliary verb (or some form of the verb *to be)* is placed before the subject. The word *not* remains in its normal position. The contracted form of the negation is used universally in writing and conversation rather than the formal long form *(did not, was not,* etc.).

John *didn't* see him.
Didn't John see him?
Why *didn't* John see him?

John *wasn't* here.
Wasn't John here?
Why *wasn't* John here?

27. *SHOULD–OUGHT*. *Should* and *ought* are important auxiliary verbs used to express obligation. They have the same meaning and can be used interchangeably. They are weaker in force than *must* and sometimes have even a negative significance. Note that *ought* is followed by the infinitive with *to.*

I *should* study tonight. (but it is possible that I will not study)
I *ought* to study tonight.

He *shouldn't* smoke so much.
He *ought* not* to smoke so much.

EXERCISES

A. *Change to question form:*

1. We weren't at the lesson yesterday. (Weren't you at the lesson yesterday?)
2. John doesn't speak English well.
3. We didn't got to the movie yesterday.
4. John doesn't have a book.
5. Mary isn't in the office.
6. She doesn't study with us.
7. They weren't at the movie with us.
8. He isn't busy.
9. She can't speak French.

---

*Note: It is not general practice to contract *ought not.*

10. They don't know how to speak Spanish.
11. She can't meet us tonight.
12. He didn't eat in the cafeteria at noon.

B. *Change to question form. Begin each sentence with the question word* WHY:

1. He didn't meet us in the cafeteria. (Why didn't he meet us in the cafeteria?)
2. John didn't come to the lesson yesterday.
3. Mary doesn't know John well.
4. They don't walk to school.
5. John and Mary don't like their teacher.
6. They weren't at the meeting last night.
7. John wasn't at the lesson this morning.
8. Mary can't come to the lesson today.
9. John couldn't meet us yesterday.
10. We didn't go to the park on Sunday.

C. *Read once using* SHOULD *and once using* OUGHT TO:

1. Helen .... (study) more. (a. Helen should study more. b. Helen ought to study more.)
2. I .... (spend) more time on my English.
3. He .... (see) a doctor immediately.
4. You .... (study) all the new words.
5. She .... (take) her medicine every day.
6. He .... (visit) his friends more often.
7. We .... (pay) more attention in class.
8. Every child .... (obey) his parents.
9. She .... (be) more careful of what she says.
10. He .... (be) more polite to strangers.

D. *Change to negative form:*

1. You should tell him about it. (You shouldn't tell him about it.)
2. She ought to mention it to him.
3. They ought to spend more money on English lessons.
4. He ought to buy a new car.
5. She should try to reduce.
6. He should join the army.
7. We should get seats in the front row.

8. You ought to call her late at night.
9. We should wait here for her.
10. He ought to go by plane.

E. *(Review) Change, first to negative form, and second to question form:*

1. Most vegetables grow on vines. (a. Most vegetables don't grow on vines. b. Do most vegetables grow on vines?)
2. Some grow in the ground.
3. Tomatoes grow on vines.
4. John was here yesterday.
5. He told me about his trip.
6. They were at the lesson this morning.
7. John can speak French well.
8. January is the first month of the year.
9. Sunday comes before Monday.
10. There are seven days in a week.
11. We paid our fare on the bus.
12. We arrived in time for the lesson.
13. He should tell her about it.
14. He told her about it.

F. *(Review) Change to question form. Begin each question with the question word in parentheses:*

1. They came to school by bus. (How) (How did they come to school?)
2. John was here at ten o'clock. (What time)
3. The bus stops near our home. (Where)
4. I got on the bus at 42nd Street. (Where)
5. We paid ten cents for it. (How much)
6. He comes to our house very often. (How often)
7. Mary can speak French. (What language)
8. There are seven days in a week. (How many)
9. There were three men in the room. (How many)
10. We rode through the park in John's car. (Where)
11. He left on the noon train. (On which train)
12. He usually eats eggs for breakfast. (What)

G. *Answer these questions:*

1. Why doesn't John attend class regularly?

2. Why didn't you come to the lesson yesterday?
3. Why don't you come to school by bus?
4. Why wasn't Helen at the lesson yesterday?
5. Why didn't she go with you to the movie last night?
6. Why can't William speak French well?
7. Why didn't you go for a walk in the park yesterday as usual?
8. Why doesn't Helen like to study English?
9. Why couldn't Helen go to the party last night with you?
10. Why didn't you prepare your lesson last night?

LESSON 16

28. FUTURE TENSE.

a) The future tense in English is formed by use of the auxiliary verb *will*. To this auxiliary the infinitive of the main verb (without *to*) is added.

I will see you tomorrow.
John will be here at noon.

b) *Will* is generally used to express promise or determination, while the phrase "to be going to" (see Book 2, Rule 72) is used to express intention or simple future action.

I will study	we will study
you will study	you will study
he, she will study	they will study

c) The contracted form of *will* is *'ll*. Thus we have the following contractions, in which we join the subject and the auxiliary verb: *I'll, you'll, he'll, she'll, it'll, we'll, they'll*, etc. These contractions are common in present-day English; in fact, the full forms are rarely heard in everyday conversation. The student should therefore practice these contractions and try to use them in his everyday speech.

I'll meet you at two o'clock.
We'll return on Wednesday.
John'll help us with the work.

d) *Will* is a regular auxiliary verb, similar in function to *can, may, must*, etc. The negative form of the future tense is thus obtained regularly by placing *not* after *shall* or *will*. The question is also obtained regularly by placing *will* before the subject.

John will come tomorrow at six.
John *will not** come tomorrow at six.
Will John come tomorrow at six?
What time will John come tomorrow?

*In conversation, instead of saying *will not*, we generally use the contraction *won't*. The contracted form is often used in writing also.

EXERCISES

A. *Supply the future tense of the verb in parentheses:*

1. John .... (come) at two o'clock tomorrow afternoon. (John will come at two o'clock tomorrow afternoon.)
2. Mary .... (go) to the movies with us.
3. We .... (get) on the bus at 70th Street.
4. Then we .... (pay) our fare.
5. I .... (go) to school by bus tomorrow.
6. I .... (eat) lunch with John tomorrow.
7. We .... (eat) in the cafeteria.
8. I don't think that Mary .... (eat) with us.
9. John .... (come) to school before us.
10. I .... (get) up early tomorrow morning.
11. I .... (see) you at the lesson.
12. John .... (speak) to Mr. Smith about our lesson.

B. *Repeat the previous exercise, using contracted forms:*

1. John .... (come) at two o'clock tomorrow afternoon. (John'll come at two o'clock tomorrow afternoon.)

C. *Change to negative form:*

1. John will meet us at two o'clock. (John won't meet us at two o'clock.)
2. They will see us at the lesson.
3. I will be back by three o'clock.
4. John will study with us tonight.
5. He will bring his books with him.
6. Mary will meet us after the lesson.
7. We will meet you in the cafeteria.
8. You will soon need a new English book.
9. They will be back soon.
10. We will leave for New York on Wednesday.

D. *Change to question form:*

1. They will study with us tomorrow. (Will they study with us tomorrow?)
2. I will meet you at two o'clock.
3. We will see you in the cafeteria.

4. They will return next month.
5. She will leave for Europe in June.
6. We will spend several weeks in France.
7. They will write to us every week.
8. John will have lunch in the cafeteria.
9. He will meet us in the cafeteria at twelve.
10. Spring will begin in a few months.
11. Winter will end in a few weeks.
12. Summer will come after spring.

E. *Supply the correct preposition:*

1. A man sees .... (with) ....his eyes.
2. What kinds .... fruit do you like?
3. He came .... the lesson .... time.
4. He was absent .... the lesson.
5. I go to school .... bus.
6. I arrive .... my school .... eight o'clock.
7. He arrived .... time .... his lesson.
8. Do you like eggs .... breakfast?
9. How many months are there .... a year?
10. Do you drink coffee .... a cup?
11. Do tomatoes grow .... the earth or .... a vine?
12. How many cups .... coffee do you drink every day?

F. *Choose the correct form:*

1. Both doors (was, were) closed. (Both doors were closed.)
2. He is (a, an) very old man.
3. John sat down and (put, puts) his feet up on a chair.
4. What time (do, did) you meet John yesterday?
5. Were you absent (in, from) class yesterday?
6. Every man (has, have) two eyes.
7. A man (see, sees) with his eyes.
8. Every day I eat (a, an) egg for breakfast.
9. There (was, were) several men in the room.
10. John (said, told) us about the new teacher.
11. This is the book (which, who) I need.
12. Does the teacher usually (speak, speaks) English in the lesson?

G. *Answer these questions:*

1. What time will you go to bed tonight?
2. What time will you get up tomorrow morning?
3. What time will you leave home tomorrow morning to go to school?
4. Will you walk to school or go by bus?
5. Will your friends go with you or will you go to school alone?
6. What time will you arrive at school?
7. What time do you arrive at school every day?
8. What time did you arrive at school yesterday?
9. What time do you eat lunch every day?
10. What time did you eat lunch yesterday?
11. What time will you eat lunch tomorrow?

LESSON 17

29. FUTURE TENSE—VERB *TO BE*.

a) The future time of the verb *to be* is formed in the same way as the future time of other verbs. To the auxiliary *will* the infinitive (without *to)* is added.

John will be here at two o'clock.
They will be back before dinner.

b) The negative of the future tense of the verb *to be* is formed regularly by placing *not* after the auxiliary *will*. The question form is also obtained regularly by placing the auxiliary before the subject.

John will be at the lesson tomorrow.
John will not be at the lesson tomorrow.
Will John be at the lesson tomorrow?
What time will John be at the lesson tomorrow?

30. *WHO—WHO—WHOSE*.

a) The objective case form of *who* (used as both a relative and an interrogative pronoun) is *whom*. We use *whom* after all prepositions, a direct object of the verb, etc.

To *whom** did he write the letter?
The man *whom*** I met was John's father.

b) The possessive case form of who is *whose*. We use *whose* in both interrogative and relative pronoun constructions as shown in the following examples:

Whose pencil is this?
The man *whose* daughter called is here now.

---

*In everyday conversation most people would state this sentence as: "*Who* did he write the letter to?" *Whom*, though grammatically correct in such sentences, is fast disappearing from present-day use, being replaced by the more convenient *who*. *Whom*, however, is still met in formal speech and particularly in writing; therefore, the form must be studied by the student, if for recognition purposes only.

**This sentence would be more often expressed in everyday conversation as "The man *who* I met was John's father," or "The man *that* I met was John's father," or even more common, "The man I met was John's father." See previous footnote.

EXERCISES

A. *Supply the future tense of the verb* TO BE *in the following:*

1. Mary .... at the lesson at two o'clock. (Mary will be at the lesson at two o'clock.)
2. Mr. Smith .... in the office when you come.
3. I .... at home tonight.
4. The book .... on the desk.
5. The students .... in the classroom.
6. The pencils .... on the table.
7. John .... in the cafeteria.
8. There .... several people in the room.
9. Mr. Smith .... in Washington tomorrow.
10. Miss Jones .... our new teacher.
11. It .... warm tomorrow.
12. I .... busy tomorrow.

B. *Change to negative form:*

1. He will be here at two o'clock. (He won't be here at two o'clock.)
2. John and Mary will be in class tomorrow.
3. There will be two more students in our class.
4. I shall be in the cafeteria at noon.
5. There will be twenty-eight days in February this year.
6. Henry will be in Washington next week.
7. This will be your room.
8. They will be here at three o'clock.
9. There will be many people there.
10. They will be at the movie with us.
11. There will be four weeks in this month.
12. I shall be here early tomorrow.

C. *Change to question form:*

1. They will be here soon. (Will they be here soon?)
2. John will be here at six o'clock.
3. I will be here later.
4. There will be two new students in our class.
5. The magazines will be on the table.
6. This will be your seat.

7. I will be back on Tuesday.
8. There will be seats for us.
9. John will be absent tomorrow.
10. He will be here on Wednesday.
11. Mary will be at the lesson tomorrow.
12. The weather will be warm tomorrow.

D. *Choose the correct form:*

1. To (who, whom) did you write a letter? (To whom did you write a letter?)
2. With (who, whom) does he want to speak?
3. (Who, whom) is the best student in your class?
4. The man (who, whom) telephoned you is my father.
5. The man (who, whom) you saw was my teacher.
6. From (who, whom) did you get this money?
7. With (who, whom) are you going to the movie?
8. The girl (who, whom) I met was very beautiful.

E. *Begin each sentence with* WHOSE:

1. This is John's book. (Whose book is this?)
2. This is my pencil.
3. This is Mary's pen.
4. This is her desk.
5. This is my room.
6. This is his notebook.
7. This is my table.
8. She is my teacher.
9. This is his office.
10. This is the teacher's chair.

F. *Change these sentences to use* WHOSE:

1. To whom does this pen belong? (*Whose* pen is this?)
2. To whom does that yellow pencil belong?
3. To whom do these books belong?
4. To whom do these magazines belong?
5. To whom does this notebook belong?
6. To whom does that coat belong?
7. To whom does that sweater belong?
8. To whom does this automobile belong?

G. *Choose the correct form:*

1. I (can, could) not come to the lesson yesterday. (I could not come to the lesson yesterday.)
2. John will (sit, sits) near us.
3. I like (walk, to walk) in the park.
4. On what day will he (begin, begins) to teach us?
5. What (do, does) the waitress usually bring John for dessert?
6. Where (do, does) the students study English?
7. Is this (a, the) book which you want?
8. John (shall, will) meet us at noon.
9. Mary (have, has) many good English books.
10. John (said, told) that he was very busy yesterday.
11. There (is, are) many pictures on the wall.
12. Yesterday I (feel, felt) very well.

H. *Answer these questions:*

1. Will you be in class tomorrow?
2. Why won't Helen be in class tomorrow?
3. What day will tomorrow be?
4. Will tomorrow be Saturday?
5. Where will you be tomorrow night at seven o'clock?
6. Are you busy today?
7. Were you busy yesterday?
8. Will you be busy tomorrow?
9. Will all the students be in class tomorrow or will some be absent?
10. Will the weather tomorrow be warm or cold?
11. How long will Mr. Smith be in Washington?

LESSON 18

31. SHORTENED ANSWER FORM. In conversational English, direct answers to questions are often given in shortened grammatical form. In these shortened forms, only the subject, always expressed by a pronoun, and the auxiliary verb are used.

Do you like New York?
Yes, I do.
No, I don't.

Does Helen speak English well?
Yes, she does.
No, she doesn't.

Did you see him yesterday?
Yes, I did.
No, I didn't.

Was the movie good?
Yes, it was.
No, it wasn't.

32. *ALSO-TOO—EITHER. The words also* or *too* cannot be used in negative sentences. These words are replaced in negatives sentences by the word *either*.

John *also* speaks English well.
John doesn't speak English well *either*.

I walk to school *too*.
I don't walk to school *either*.

33. *WHY—WHAT FOR.* We often substitute *what for* in place of *why* in direct questions in English. Note, however, that in such cases we always put *what* at the beginning of the sentence and *for* at the end of the sentence.

Why did he go there?
or *What* did he go there *for*?

Why did you say that?
or *What* did you say that *for*?

EXERCISES

A. *Give only shortened answers (as explained under Rule 31) to the following:*

1. Does your teacher speak English well? (Yes, he does)
2. Can you speak French?
3. Does your teacher live in New York City?
4. Do you live in New York City?

5. Can the students in your class speak English well?
6. Does summer always come after spring?
7. Did you study your lesson last night?
8. Did you have an English lesson today?
9. Do you smoke?
10. Does your teacher smoke?
11. Is today Wednesday?
12. Was yesterday Thursday?

B. *Change to negative form:*

1. John also likes New York. (John doesn't like New York either.)
2. Mary can speak English well too.
3. I also eat in the cafeteria.
4. John walks to school too.
5. She comes here also.
6. John went to the movie with us also.
7. He liked the picture too.
8. I also eat lunch at one o'clock.
9. Mary also likes pie for dessert.
10. He goes to the restaurant on the corner too.
11. I like to eat there too.
12. I ate there yesterday too.

C. *Substitute* WHAT FOR *for* WHY *in these sentences. Be sure to put* WHAT *at the beginning of the sentence and* FOR *at the end:*

1. Why did you do such a thing? (What did you do such a thing for?)
2. Why did she want to go there?
3. Why did John do that?
4. Why did William bring his sister along with him?
5. Why does he want to study French?
6. Why do you want to go to Chicago?
7. Why did she give him so much money?
8. Why did he stay away so long?
9. Why did you get up so early this morning?
10. Why did you give the waiter such a big tip?

D. *Substitute* WHY *in place of* WHAT FOR:

1. What did the child run away for? (Why did the child run away?)
2. What does she want to see him for?
3. What does he say such foolish things for?
4. What does he want to study engineering for?
5. What does he spend so much time there for?
6. What did Mr. Smith go to New York for?
7. What did he get up so early for ?
8. What does she walk in the park every afternoon for?

E. *(Review) Change to past time (yesterday) and to future time (tomorrow):*

1. John goes to that restaurant every day. (a. John went to that restaurant yesterday. b. John will go to that restaurant tomorrow.)
2. He sits at the same table every day.
3. The waitress brings him a menu.
4. He looks at the menu.
5. He orders his lunch and some dessert.
6. The waitress then brings him a check.
7. John pays the check.
8. Later he leaves the restaurant.
9. I eat in the same restaurant with John.
10. I also sit at the same table.
11. We always do the same thing after lunch.
12. We take a walk in the park.

F. *Supply the correct article where necessary:*

1. There is .... book on .... table in .... first picture. (There is a book on the table in the first picture.)
2. There is .... basket under .... table.
3. John will not be at .... lesson tomorrow.
4. He will go to .... Washington.
5. First, he will go to .... Pennsylvania Station.
6. Do you like .... New York City?
7. John often goes to .... restaurant on .... corner.
8. He asks .... waitress for .... menu.

9. He drinks .... glass of .... milk.
10. He orders .... piece of .... pie for .... dessert.
11. Next he pays .... check and leaves .... restaurant.
12. What do you usually eat for .... dessert?

G. *Choose the correct form:*

1. I don't like this exercise (also, either). (I don't like this exercise either.)
2. John speaks French well (too, either).
3. There (was, were) many people in the park today.
4. (Did, does) John walk home with you yesterday?
5. Does a man (hear, hears) with his eyes or with his ears?
6. They (was, were) not at the lesson yesterday.
7. I (can, could) not meet you last night.
8. Mary (said, told) that she was sick.
9. How many pencils (has, have) William?
10. Does summer (come, comes) before or after spring?
11. Whose books are (this, these)?
12. I want (a, an) English book.

LESSON 19

34. *THIS-THAT; THESE-THOSE.* The plural form of *this* is *these. This* and *these* refer to things near at hand. The plural form of *that* is *those. That* and *those* refer to things at a distance.

This book is mine.
These books are mine.

That book over there on the table is John's.
Those books over there on the table are John's.

35. EXPRESSIONS OF NECESSITY *(HAVE TO).*

a) Necessity or strong obligation in English may be expressed by *must* or *have to* (*have* plus an infinitive). *Must,* however, appears to be in use today for expression of orders, commands, or very strong obligation on the part of the speaker. *Have to* seems more in use for everyday expressions of necessity. In many cases, however, both *must* and *have to* have the same meaning.

I *must* go to the hospital to see my friend.
I *have to* go to the hospital to see my friend.

John *must* work tonight.
John *has to* work tonight.

b) Since *must* has no past form, obligation or necessity in the past is expressed only by the past form of *have to.*

I *had to* study last night.
John *had to* work very late yesterday.

c) Necessity or obligation in the future is similarly expressed by the future tense of *have to.*

He *will have to* work tonight.
You *will have to* wait a few minutes.

EXERCISES

A. *Fill in the blanks with* THIS *or* THESE:

1. ....book is mine. (This book is mine.)
2. .... apples are not good.
3. .... gentleman wishes to see you.

4. .... books are not interesting.
5. .... magazine belongs to you.
6. .... letter is for you.
7. Please mail .... letters for me.
8. Do you know .... boy?
9. .... girls are Mr. Smith's daughters.
10. .... room is too small for our group.
11. May we use .... rooms today for our lessons?
12. .... pictures are quite beautiful.

B. *Fill in the blanks with* THAT *or* THOSE:

1. ....pencil on the desk is not mine. (That pencil on the desk is not mine.)
2. Whose books are ....?
3. .... book belongs to the teacher.
4. .... chairs are not comfortable.
5. .... men in the office are my friends.
6. .... pictures on the wall are a little too large.
7. .... rooms are very dark.
8. .... flowers are beautiful.
9. .... book is not interesting.
10. Will you please mail .... letters on the table?
11. .... restaurant across the street is not good.
12. I don't like .... sandwiches which we had for lunch.

C. *Substitute the correct form of* HAVE TO *for* MUST *in the following:*

1. I must work tonight. (I have to work tonight.)
2. John must go out of town this afternoon.
3. You must read this article.
4. Mary and John must visit their friend who is in the hospital.
5. They must stay there at least an hour.
6. I must get up early every day.
7. We must write a composition each night.
8. I must write many letters.
9. We must prepare our lessons every night.
10. Mary must study French next year.
11. John must also take another language.
12. We must learn many new words every day.

D. *Read the following with* MUST. *Then change to past and future time:*

1. I .... leave at once. (a. I must leave at once. b. I had to leave at once. c. I will have to leave at once.)
2. He .... go to the hospital right away.
3. We .... make reservations at once.
4. He .... learn all the new words.
5. We .... hurry in order to get there early.
6. He .... spend more time on his English.
7. She .... attend class every day.
8. I .... answer this letter at once.
9. We .... telephone her right away.
10. He .... stay at home and rest.

E. *Change to past and future time:*

1. I have to work today.
2. John has to be here at two o'clock.
3. Mary has to come with him.
4. We have to study tonight.
5. They have to write many letters.
6. You have to wait a few minutes.
7. They have to come back later.
8. We all have to write a composition for our English lesson.
9. We have to go to the hospital this afternoon.
10. He has to see a doctor.
11. John has to stop his English lessons.
12. I have to get up early.

F. *Choose the correct form:*

1. I don't like (that, those) apples. (I don't like those apples.)
2. Yesterday I (must, had to) work very hard.
3. John and Mary (was, were) at the movie last night.
4. Mary (said, told) the teacher she could not prepare her lesson.
5. John said that he (can, could) not come to the lesson yesterday.
6. Mr. Reese is (a, an) Englishman.
7. John didn't go to the movie (also, either).
8. They (shall, will) be here very soon.

9. What time (do, does) your English lesson begin?
10. Does a man (see, sees) with his eyes or with his ears?
11. What color (is, are) cherries?
12. Where did John (eat, eats) lunch yesterday?

G. *Answer these questions:*

1. What time do you have to get up every morning?
2. What time did you have to get up yesterday morning?
3. What time will you have to get up tomorrow morning?
4. How much time do you have to spend on your English lessons every night?
5. Do you have to write many or a few compositions for your English class?
6. When was the last time that you had to write a composition for your English class?

LESSON 20

36. *HAVE TO* (NEGATIVE AND QUESTION FORM).

a) When *to have* is used with an infinitive to show necessity or obligation, we obtain the negative* in the same way as we do for all regular verbs, that is, by using the auxiliaries *do, does, did.*

I have to work tonight.
I *don't* have to work tonight.

I had to work last night.
I *didn't* have to work last night.

b) Similarly, the question form of *to have,* when used with an infinitive to show necessity or obligation, is formed with the auxiliaries *do, does, did.*

He has to work tonight.
Does he have to work tonight?
Why *does* he have to work tonight?

I had to work last night.
Did you have to work last night?
Why *did* you have to work last night?

37. COMPARISON OF ADJECTIVES.

a) The comparative degree of all adjectives of one syllable (and a few of two syllables) is obtained by adding *er* to the positive degree (big, bigger; small, smaller, etc.). The comparative degree is aways followed by *than.*

New York is bigger *than* Washington.
Mary is older *than* John.

b) If, however, an adjective has more than two syllables, the comparative degree is formed by the use of *more.*

Positive	*Comparative*
beautiful	more beautiful
interesting	more interesting

*The difference in feeling between *must* and *have to* (see explanation under Rule 35) is more clearly seen in negative sentences. Thus, "John must work tonight" and "John has to work tonight" have more or less the same meaning. However, "John must not work tonight" is more a command, forbidding John to work, while "John does not have to work tonight" means that, since perhaps today is a holiday, it isn't necessary for John to work tonight.

c) A few adjectives have special comparative forms:

Positive	*Comparative*
good	better
bad	worse
far	farther
little	less
many	more

EXERCISES

A. *Change to negative form:*

1. They have to study very hard. (They don't have to study very hard.)
2. He had to be there at two o'clock.
3. We have to get up early.
4. We have to write a composition tonight.
5. We had to meet him at noon.
6. Mr. Smith has to go out of town.
7. They had to leave early.
8. I have to buy a new pen.
9. We have to work on Sunday.
10. John had to go to the hospital.
11. We have to prepare our homework every day.
12. We will have to learn many new words.

B. *Change to question form:*

1. He had to leave at noon. (Did he have to leave at noon?)
2. We have to get up early every morning.
3. They have to study every day.
4. They have to rent a new apartment.
5. He had to buy several new books.
6. He had to leave a tip for the waiter.
7. He had to return yesterday.
8. He will have to wait a few minutes.
9. They will have to come back later.
10. He has to ride the bus to school every day.
11. She has to have more fresh air.
12. He has to take more exercise.

C. *Change the sentences in Section B to question form again, but this time begin each question with some question word like* WHEN, WHERE, WHAT TIME, WHY, etc.

D. *Change to past time and to future time:*

1. He doesn't have to leave right away. (a. He didn't have to leave right away. b. He won't have to leave right away.)
2. We don't have to get there early.
3. They don't have to go by plane.
4. She doesn't have to return until Wednesday.
5. They don't have to move to a new apartment.
6. I don't have to study very hard.
7. We don't have to write many compositions.
8. I don't have to buy many new books.
9. He doesn't have to walk to his work.
10. You don't have to leave early.

E. *Change to past time and to future time:*

1. Do you have to leave early? (a. Did you have to leave early? b. Will you have to leave early?)
2. Does he have to return to the hospital?
3. Do you have to speak to the teacher about it?
4. Do you have to learn many new words?
5. Do you have to send it by airmail?
6. Does she have to stay at home and rest?
7. Does he have to telephone to her every day?
8. Do you have to take a taxi to your work every day?
9. Does she have to go on a diet?
10. Does he have to tell everyone about it?

F. *Supply the comparative form of the adjective in parentheses:*

1. Philadelphia is .... (large) .... Washington. (Philadelphia is larger than Washington.)
2. John is .... (short) .... William.
3. Henry is .... (tall) .... I.
4. This book is .... (old) .... that one.
5. The weather today is .... (bad) .... yesterday.

6. This summer is .... (hot) .... last summer.
7. This article is .... (interesting) .... that one.
8. Is this exercise .... (difficult) .... the last one?
9. These apples are .... (good) .... those.
10. Some people are .... (healthy) .... others.
11. This room is .... (light) .... that one.
12. Is this exercise .... (important) .... the last one?

G. *Complete these sentences by using the adjective which is the opposite of the one in italics:*

1. Henry is not *taller* than I; Henry is .... (Henry is not *taller* than I; Henry is *shorter* than I.)
2. New York is not *smaller* than Chicago; New York is ....
3. Helen is not *younger* than her sister; Helen is ....
4. This street is not *wider* than that street; this street is ....
5. This exercise is not *more difficult* than the last one; this exercise is ....
6. This book is not *thicker* than my French book; this book is ....
7. This book was not *more expensive* than my French book; this book was ....
8. The weather today is not *better* than it was yesterday; the weather today is ....
9. The weather today is not *colder* than it was yesterday; the weather today is ....

H. *Choose the correct form:*

1. Chicago is (more big, bigger) than Philadelphia. (Chicago is bigger than Philadelphia.)
2. We (don't have to, haven't to) work tomorrow because it is a holiday.
3. There (was, were) many people at the meeting.
4. Mary (said, told) us several interesting stories.
5. This is the building (who, which) I (said, told) you about.
6. We drink coffee (in, from) a cup.

7. (Does, do) all these books belong to you?
8. This magazine is more interesting (than, as) the other.
9. (That, those) books belong to Henry.
10. John (hadn't to, didn't have to) come to class yesterday.
11. Give me (a, an) apple and (a, an) peach.
12. (These, those) boys on the other side of the street are students.

I. *Answer these questions:*

1. Are you taller or shorter than your friend?
2. Is Mary taller or shorter than her sister?
3. Is this exercise easier or more difficult than the last exercise?
4. Is English grammar easier or more difficult than Spanish grammar?
5. Is the weather today colder or warmer than the weather yesterday?
6. Is the bus faster or slower than a taxi?
7. Did you pay less money or more money for your English book than for your other books?
8. Was your English book more expensive or less expensive than your history book?

LESSON 21

38. COMPARISON OF ADJECTIVES—SUPERLATIVE DEGREE.

a) The superlative degree of all adjectives of one syllable (and a few of two syllables) is formed by adding *est* to the positive degree (big, biggest; small, smallest). The definite article *the* is always used with the superlative degree.

John is the tallest student in the class.
New York is the largest city in the United States.

b) With the adjectives of more than two syllables the superlative degree is formed with *most.* (See similar formation of comparative degree with *more,* Rule 37B.)

This is the most interesting book in our library.
John is the most intelligent student in the class.

c) A few adjectives have special superlative forms:

Positive	*Comparative*	*Superlative*
good	better	best
bad	worse	worst
far	farther	farthest
little	less	least
many	more	most

EXERCISES

A. *In the following, introduce the superlative form of the adjective in parentheses:*

1. John is .... (tall) boy in the class. (John is the tallest boy in the class.)
2. Today is .... (hot) day of the year.
3. New York is .... (interesting) city in the United States.
4. New York is also .... (large) city in the United States.
5. This apple is .... (sweet) of all.
6. This park is .... (beautiful) in the city.
7. John is .... (intelligent) boy in the class.
8. He is also .... (good) student in the class.
9. Henry is .... (bad) dancer in the school.
10. Which is .... (large) city in the country?

11. This room is .... (light) in the whole building.
12. Which student in your class knows .... (many) English words?

B. *State the adjectives in parentheses, first in comparative form, and second in superlative form. Use words of your choosing to complete each sentence:*

1. Henry is .... (tall) .... (a. Henry is taller than George. b. Henry is the tallest boy in the school.)
2. Grace is .... (pretty) ....
3. William is .... (intelligent) ....
4. This book is .... (interesting) ....
5. Frank is .... (young) ....
6. The World Trade Center is .... (tall) ....
7. The Mississippi River is .... (long) ....
8. This street is .... (wide) ....
9. John is a .... (good) student ....
10. This exercise is .... (easy) ....

C. *Change to introduce the correct form of* HAVE TO*:*

1. It is necessary for him to leave early. (He has to leave early.)
2. It was necessary for him to get up at six o'clock.
3. It will be necessary for him to wait.
4. It is necessary for them to take an early train.
5. It will be necessary for you to sit here a while.
6. It is not necessary for them to come early.
7. It was not necessary for me to telephone to him.
8. It was necessary for us to go by bus.
9. It will be necessary for all of you to write a composition for tomorrow.
10. It was not necessary for him to go by plane.
11. Is it necessary for us to come back later?
12. Was it necessary for you to speak to him about it?

D. *Supply the correct preposition:*

1. What did you eat .... dessert? (What did you eat for dessert?)
2. He sat .... our table.
3. He looked .... the menu.
4. Do potatoes grow .... the earth or .... a vine?

5. Will she be .... the lesson tomorrow?
6. These are the most beautiful .... all.
7. We live .... an apartment.
8. They keep food .... their cellar.
9. He studies .... the morning.
10. He went .... the movie .... us.
11. He was late .... the lesson.
12. He goes to school .... bus.

E. *Choose the correct form:*

1. William is the (biggest, most big) boy in the class. (William is the biggest boy in the class.)
2. Yesterday we (hadn't to, didn't have to) come to school.
3. Helen is taller (as, than) her sister.
4. How many books (does, do) they have?
5. We waited (a, an) whole hour for you.
6. When will John (go, goes) to Chicago?
7. Mary will soon (study, studies) in our class.
8. They can't speak English (either, also).
9. He needs (a, an) new English book.
10. John (can, could) not come to class yesterday.
11. Whose pencils are (these, this)?
12. The weather today is (more better, better) than the weather yesterday.

F. *Answer these questions:*

1. Is New York City larger or smaller than Chicago?
2. What is the largest city in the United States?
3. What is the largest city in England?
4. What is the largest city in the world today?
5. What is the most interesting subject which you study in school?
6. Do you find languages more interesting or less interesting than mathematics?
7. What is the most difficult subject which you study at school?
8. Is the Pacific Ocean larger or smaller than the Atlantic Ocean?
9. What is the largest ocean in the world?
10. Who is the tallest student in your English class?

LESSON 22

39. Comparison of Adjectives—Equality.

a) Equality in comparison of adjectives is expressed in English by the use of *as* before and after the adjective as shown in the following examples:

John is *as* tall *as* Henry.
This book is *as* good *as* that one.

b) The negative form of such comparisons may be expressed with *so* . . . *as* or *as* . . . *as,* although *as* . . . *as* is more common.

John is not *as (so)* tall *as* Henry.
This book is not *as* good *as* that one.

40. Use of Infinitives. The student should note the various ways in which we use infinitives in English:

a) Certain verbs such as *like, want, wish, hope* often need an infinitive to complete their meaning.

I like *to swim.*
He wants *to go* with us.

b) Infinitives often follow certain adjectives, serving to complete their meaning.

It is *easy to learn* these rules.
It will be *necessary to leave* soon.

EXERCISES

A. *Give shortened negative answers to the following:*

1. Did John go to the movie last night? (No, he didn't).
2. Were you at the movie last night?
3. Will you be in class tomorrow?
4. Can you speak French?
5. Does John speak English well?
6. Did it rain yesterday?
7. Does it rain every day?
8. Do you go to school by bus?
9. Could you understand what he said?
10. Was yesterday Monday?

11. Did you study last night?
12. Will you eat lunch at noon?

B. *Rewrite each sentence to show equality of comparison. State each sentence first in positive form and then in negative form:*

1. John is taller than his brother. (a. John is as tall as his brother. b. John isn't as tall as his brother.)
2. This street is wider than that one.
3. This exercise is longer than the last.
4. Helen is more beautiful than Mary.
5. New York is more important a city than Washington.
6. Our apartment is larger than yours.
7. This corridor is larger than the room.
8. The sky is darker than it was yesterday.
9. This book is better than the other.
10. The weather today is worse than it was yesterday.
11. John makes more mistakes than Henry.
12. There are more sentences in this exercise than in the last one.

C. *Use your own words to complete these sentences. Be sure to use an infinitive construction in each case:*

1. Helen wants to .... (Helen wants to go to the movies with us.)
2. She likes to ....
3. George says that he wants to ....
4. They hope to ....
5. There is a man in the office who wishes to ....
6. I like to ....
7. Do you want to ....
8. He hopes to ....
9. Helen loves to ....
10. We both like to ....

D. *Use your own words to complete these sentences. Be sure to use an infinitive construction in each case:*

1. It is difficult to .... (It is difficult to learn English well.)
2. It is necessary to ....

3. It is hard for me to ....
4. It is easy for Margaret to ....
5. It was very kind of you to ....
6. I am glad to ....
7. It was funny to ....
8. It is too late to ....
9. It is too cold to ....
10. I'll be happy to ....

E. *Choose the correct form:*

1. New York is bigger (than, as) Chicago. (New York is bigger than Chicago.)
2. The weather today is (more bad, worse) than it was yesterday.
3. John (said, told) that he was very busy yesterday.
4. What time (does, did) your lesson begin yesterday?
5. I didn't like that movie (either, also).
6. He is the man (who, which) asked for you.
7. Mary and John (was, were) not at the lesson yesterday.
8. Does spring (come, comes) before or after summer?
9. (These, those) pencils over there on the table are mine.
10. Is (this, those) your book or John's?
11. This is (a, an) English book.
12. We (don't have to, haven't to) study because we have no lesson tomorrow.

F. *Answer these questions. Give negative answers only:*

1. Do you speak English well? (No, I don't speak English well.)
2. Can Helen speak English well?
3. Did you arrive at school on time this morning?
4. Were you in class yesterday?
5. Will you be in class tomorrow?
6. Did you prepare your lesson last night?
7. Will you walk to school tomorrow?
8. Are you in the same class as John?
9. Was yesterday Saturday?
10. Will tomorrow be Sunday?
11. Is John a good student?
12. Were the students pleased with their marks on the last examination?

LESSON 23

41. *SOME—ANY*. We generally use *some* only in positive sentences. In negative and interrogative sentences we use *any* instead of *some*.*

He has *some* friends in Chicago.
He doesn't have *any* friends in Chicago.
Does he have *any* friends in Chicago?

42. POSITION OF INDIRECT OBJECTS.

a) If, in English, the indirect object comes after the direct object, the preposition *to* is used before the indirect object.

Henry gave the book to me.
Helen sent some flowers to us.

b) If, however, the indirect object comes before the direct object, the preposition *to* is not used before the indirect object.

Henry gave me the book.
Helen sent us some flowers.

43. USE OF INFINITIVES (Continued). In the last lesson (see Rule 40), we saw how infinitives are often used to complete the meaning of certain verbs and adjectives in English. We also use the infinitive in English to express the idea of purpose. We may use an infinitive alone in this construction or with *in order to*. Examples:

He went to Chicago in order to see his friend.
or He went to Chicago *to see* his friend.

EXERCISES

A. *Change to negative form:*

1. He has some money. (He doesn't have any money.)
2. John gave me some good advice.

**Some*, although never used in negative sentences, is sometimes used in questions when a positive answer is expected. Thus, "Do you need *some* money?" rather suggests that a positive answer will be given, indicating perhaps the amount of money needed. This distinction in meaning, however, is a subtle one and need not concern the beginning student at this time. It is equally correct to say "Do you need *any* money?"

3. There are some chairs in the room.
4. I have some books with me.
5. He has some time to study.
6. I wrote some letters last night.
7. I saw some men in the office.
8. There are some pictures on the wall.
9. Put some flowers in the vase.
10. Give some money to him.
11. Bring some money with you.
12. I took some friends with me.

B. *Change to question form:*

1. He saw some people in the room. (Did he see any people in the room?)
2. He has some friends in Washington.
3. There are some books on the table.
4. I put some chairs in the room.
5. There are some famous cities in Canada.
6. I found some answers in the back of the book.
7. We picked some apples from the tree.
8. I bought some new books yesterday.
9. There are some students in the corridor.
10. I brought some friends with me.
11. We read some articles in this magazine every day.
12. He has some cigarettes.

C. *Place the indirect object before the direct object:*

1. He gave the money to me. (He gave me the money.)
2. She brought the book to me.
3. He sent a letter to me.
4. He told the story to us.
5. The teacher gave some dictation to us.
6. He sent some candy to his sister.
7. He sent two cables to her.
8. He gave a ring to his friend.
9. They sent an invitation to us.
10. John lent some money to his friends.
11. Will you lend your pen to me?
12. He gave some excellent advice to all of us.

D. *Place the indirect object after the direct object:*

1. He gave me some books. (He gave some books to me.)
2. They gave us some magazines.
3. He sent his mother several letters.
4. They brought us many presents from abroad.
5. I gave him the note which you sent.
6. Please give us some dictation today.
7. They sent us invitations to the party.
8. Henry told us the story of his trip.
9. John gladly lent me the money.
10. Please lend me your pencil for a few minutes.
11. They sent us the material right away.
12. Please hand me that book.

E. *Instead of* IN ORDER TO, *use the simple infinitive to express the idea of purpose:*

1. He went there in order to talk with the teacher. (He went there to talk with the teacher.)
2. He came to our home in order to see my father.
3. He ran to the store in order to buy the newspaper.
4. He stopped at the office in order to pick up some letters.
5. He drew a picture of a cow in order to explain to the waiter what he wanted.
6. He went to the movie in order to pass the time.
7. He called by telephone in order to wish me a happy birthday.
8. They are leaving early in the morning in order to get there before evening.

F. *Introduce* IN ORDER TO *in place of the simple infinitive:*

1. We went there to see our friend. (We went there in order to see our friend.)
2. He came to the station to see us off.
3. He stopped at the post office to buy some stamps.
4. She went to the store to buy some groceries.
5. He went to the hospital to see a sick friend.
6. He came here to find work.
7. He goes there every day to practice his English.
8. He studied hard to pass his examinations.

9. We often go there just to pass time.
10. We went to his home to speak with him in person.

G. *Choose the correct form:*

1. He wants (go, to go) with us to the park. (He wants to go with us to the park.)
2. William is a better student (as, than) Henry.
3. I don't have (some, any) time to talk to you.
4. They (live, lives) in New York City.
5. We haven't enough time to go there (either, also).
6. John (said, told) us he was a very good student.
7. He said he (can, could) not come to the meeting last night.
8. There (was, were) many people at the meeting.
9. What time will John (return, returns) tomorrow?
10. John is (a, an) Englishman.
11. They will stay in New York (for, during) six months.
12. Do you go to school (by, on) bus?

LESSON 24

44. Idiomatic Phrase—*IT TAKES*.

a) Duration of an action is frequently expressed in English by the impersonal *it takes* or *it took*.

It takes me twenty minutes to walk to work.
It takes John two hours to prepare his homework.

It took me twenty minutes to walk to school yesterday.
It took John two hours to prepare his homework last night.

b) The negative and interrogative forms of the impersonal *it takes* or *it took* are obtained regularly by use of the usual auxiliaries *does* and *did*.

It doesn't take me twenty minutes to walk to work.
Does it take you twenty minutes to walk to work?

45. Special Plural Forms.

a) Under Rule 3 it was stated that the plural of English nouns is obtained by adding *s* to the singular form. Words ending in an *s* sound, however, (s, sh, ch, etc.) form their plural by adding *es* to the singular.

one church	two churches
one class	two classes
one dash	two dashes

b) If a word ends in *o* preceded by a consonant, the ending *es* is added to form the plural. (Exceptions: pianos, solos, banjos.)

tomato	tomatoes
potato	potatoes

c) If a word ends in *o* preceded by a vowel, only *s* is added.

radio	radios
folio	folios

d) Most words ending in *f* or *fe* change the *f* or *fe* to *ves* in the plural.

wife	wives
knife	knives
leaf	leaves

e) Note also the following special plural forms:

child	children
fish	fish
tooth	teeth
foot	feet

EXERCISES

A. *Change the following to introduce* IT TAKES *or* IT TOOK:

1. I come to work on the bus in ten minutes. (It takes me ten minutes to come to work on the bus.)
2. I did my exercise in one hour.
3. I walked to the station in fifteen minutes.
4. We drove to Philadelphia in one hour.
5. I found my mistake in a few minutes.
6. I do my homework every night in a short time.
7. They will build the bridge in two years.
8. She learned to speak English in only one year.
9. I finished the work in an hour.
10. I wrote the letter in a few minutes.
11. They will complete the work in six years.
12. He does his homework every day in one hour.

B. *Change to negative and to interrogative form:*

1. It took him a long time to go there. (a. It didn't take him a long time to go there. b. Did it take him a long time to go there?)
2. It takes me seven minutes to walk there.
3. It took them many years to build the road.
4. It takes me only ten minutes to go there by subway.
5. It took him several hours to finish it.
6. It took a month to complete the work.
7. It will take a long time to get there.
8. It will take you a week to read this book.
9. It took them two days to find him.
10. It takes an hour to do this exercise.
11. It takes much time to learn English.
12. It took an hour to discover the mistake.

C. *Change the above sentences, in Section B, to interrogative form again. This time begin each question with* HOW LONG: (Example: 1. *How long* did it take him to go there?)

D. *Complete the following with words of your own choosing:*

1. It took me .... (It took me an hour to prepare my homework.)
2. It takes John ....
3. It won't take her ....
4. It took them ....
5. It takes only ....
6. It will take ....
7. It took us ....
8. It doesn't take ....
9. How long did it take ....
10. How long will it take ....
11. It takes Mr. Smith only ....
12. Will it take ....
13. It didn't take us ....
14. It shouldn't take more than ....

E. *Change the italicized words in the following to plural form and introduce* SOME, MANY, SEVERAL, *or* VARIOUS *in place of the indefinite article. Then make whatever other changes are necessary:*

1. There is a *church* near my home. (There are *several churches* near my home.)
2. He has a *child.*
3. I picked a *tomato* from the vine.
4. We saw a *fish* in the river.
5. I ate a *potato.*
6. I attend an English *class* every day.
7. There is a *piano* in the room.
8. There is a *door* in John's class.
9. The table is one *foot* long.
10. I have a *watch.*
11. There is a *man* in the room.
12. A *leaf* fell from the tree.

F. *(Review) Change to past and future time:*

1. John writes many letters to his friends. (a. John wrote many letters to his friends. b. John will write many letters to his friends.)
2. He first goes to his room.

3. Then he sits at his desk.
4. He begins his letter "Dear Carlos."
5. He tells Carlos that he feels well.
6. He finishes his letter and signs his name.
7. Then he folds the letter.
8. Next, he puts the letter into an envelope.
9. He then addresses the letter.
10. Next, he puts a stamp on the letter.
11. On the back of the letter he puts his return address.
12. He mails the letter on his way to school.

G. *(Review) Supply the correct indefinite or definite article where necessary:*

1. There are many countries in .... world. (There are many countries in the world.)
2. .... France is located on .... continent of .... Europe.
3. .... United States is located on .... continent of .... North America.
4. .... people of .... Soviet Union speak Russian.
5. Most of .... people in .... South America speak .... Spanish.
6. .... Spanish language is easy to learn.
7. Can you speak .... French?
8. .... French people are very polite.
9. There isn't .... telephone in .... room.
10. John wasn't in .... class yesterday.

H. *Choose the correct word:*

1. John worked there (for, during) three years. (John worked there for three years.)
2. Every man has two (feet, feets).
3. John gave (me, to me) the book.
4. I didn't see (any, some) people there.
5. The teacher (said, told) us about his trip to the museum.
6. Where (do, does) John live?
7. How many days (is, are) there in a week?
8. Were you absent (in, from) class yesterday?
9. Every day I eat (a, an) apple for my lunch.

10. I have two (radioes, radios) in my home.
11. I picked two (tomatoes, tomatos) from the vines.
12. John brought (to me, me) the package.

I. *Answer these questions:*

1. How long does it take you each night to prepare your English lessons?
2. How long did it take you last night to prepare your English lessons?
3. How long will it take you tomorrow night to prepare your English lessons?
4. How long does it take you to go to school by bus?
5. Does it take you longer to go by bus or by taxi?
6. How long does it take you to walk to school?
7. How long does it take to fly from Mexico City to New York?
8. How long does it take you to eat lunch every day?
9. How long did it take you to eat lunch yesterday?
10. How long will it take you to eat lunch tomorrow?

LESSON 25

46. *SOMEONE, ANYONE,* etc. Under Rule 41 it was stated that *some* is used generally only in positive sentences, *any* in negative and interrogative sentences. Likewise, the derivatives of *some* (someone, somebody, somewhere, something, etc.) are used normally only in positive sentences. *Anyone, anybody, anywhere, anything* are used in negative and interrogative sentences.*

I saw someone in the room.
I didn't see *anyone* in the room.
Did you see *anyone* in the room?

He brought me something to eat.
He didn't bring me *anything* to eat.
Did he bring you *anything* to eat?

47. USE OF AUXILIARY VERB *MAY*.

a) The auxiliary verb *may* is generally used in writing to show permission, as distinguished from *can* which indicates the physical ability to perform some act. In spoken American English, *can* is also used to indicate permission or consent.

You *may* smoke here.
He *can* do the work easily. It is not difficult.

b) *May* is also used, however, to show doubt or possible future action.

It is possible John is sick.
John *may* be sick.

It is possible he will come later.
He *may* come later.

EXERCISES

A. *Change to negative form:*

1. There is someone in the room. (There isn't anyone in the room.)

*Words derived from *some* (someone, something, etc.), although never used in negative sentences, are sometimes used in questions when a positive answer is expected. Thus, "Is there *someone* in the room?" rather suggests that the speaker is aware that there is someone in the room but wishes to know who it is. (See footnote to Rule 43.)

2. I saw somebody in the corridor.
3. Put it somewhere in this room.
4. There is someone at the door.
5. He lives somewhere in New York.
6. He told someone about it.
7. He gave the book to somebody.
8. I put it somewhere in this drawer.
9. Tell somebody about it.
10. He said something to her.
11. He has something to do.
12. She lost her purse somewhere in the park.

B. *Change to question form:*

1. I saw somebody at the desk. (Did you see anybody at the desk?)
2. He went somewhere last night.
3. She has something to do.
4. He told somebody about it.
5. She put it somewhere.
6. There is someone in the next room.
7. Somebody wants to speak to him.
8. I saw somebody I knew.
9. He brought something with him.
10. He gave it to someone.
11. He took them somewhere on Long Island.
12. I liked something about her.

C. *Rewrite the following* "NO" *sentences in the more common* "NOT—ANY" *negative form:*

1. They found nobody at home. (They did *not* find *anybody* at home.)
2. There is no more coffee.
3. They want nothing to drink.
4. There is nowhere for him to sit.
5. She spoke to no one about it.
6. I want no more, thank you.
7. He can see nothing without his glasses.
8. We saw nobody at all in the park.
9. They gave us nothing to eat.
10. We went nowhere after the dance.

11. He has no place to stay.
12. There was nobody in Mr. Smith's office.

D. *Change to introduce the verb* MAY:

1. It is possible that he will arrive later. (He may arrive later.)
2. It is possible that John will be late.
3. It is possible Helen will come with him.
4. It is possible that they will not come at all.
5. It is possible that the weather will not be warm.
6. Possibly Henry is out of town.
7. Possibly he doesn't know anything about it.
8. Possibly they are not at home.
9. Perhaps the book is out of date.
10. Perhaps he will not notice it.
11. Possibly they will arrive on time.
12. It is possible that the train is late.

E. *Choose the correct form:*

1. I didn't see (anyone, someone) in the room. (I didn't see anyone in the room.)
2. We didn't go (anywhere, somewhere) last night.
3. We didn't find (some, any) money in the purse.
4. John (may come, may be come) later in the day.
5. They didn't like the movie and we didn't (also, either).
6. My hat was more expensive (as, than) Helen's.
7. (These, this) pencils are of poor quality.
8. (These, those) men on the other side of the street are military officers.
9. Last week I (must, had to) go to the dentist.
10. They (said, told) us that they liked the movie very much.
11. He didn't tell (anyone, someone) about it.
12. There isn't (someone, anyone) at the door.

F. *Answer these questions. Give two answers to each question, one positive and one negative:*

1. Did you see anyone in Mr. Smith's office? (a. No, I didn't see anyone in Mr. Smith's office. b. Yes, I saw someone in Mr. Smith's office.)
2. Have you any money with you?

3. Did you tell anyone about it?
4. Did you go anywhere after the movie?
5. Did John say anything to you about it?
6. Are there any students in the hall?
7. Did the teacher find any mistakes in your composition?
8. Did anyone telephone me while I was out?
9. Does Helen know anything about mathematics?
10. Did they go anywhere after the party?
11. Did you bring any money with you?

G. *Answer these questions, using* MAY. *Add* "I'M NOT SURE" *at the end of each of your answers. Follow the form of the sample answer given:*

1. Will John help us with the work? (John *may* help us with the work—*I'm not sure.)*
2. Will Henry pass his examinations?
3. Is Mary in the garden?
4. Will Mr. Smith be back before noon?
5. Will you go to Mexico again on your next vacation?
6. Will you go by plane?
7. Will you visit other South American countries?
8. Do Mr. and Mrs. Smith own a car?
9. Do they own their own home?
10. Does he teach in the university?
11. Does Henry have any friends in Chicago?
12. Will Grace want to go with us to the party?

LESSON 26

48. Present Tense—Simple and Continuous Forms.

a) The simple form of the present tense in English is used to describe an action which goes on every day or in general.

John *reads* the newspaper every day.
It often *rains* in April.

b) The continuous form of the present tense is used to describe an action which goes on or continues at the present moment.

John *is reading* the newspaper now.
Look! It *is raining.*

c) The continuous form of the present tense of verbs is formed as follows: to the verb *to be,* used as an auxiliary, there is added the present participle (*ing* form) of the main verb.

I'm working	we're working
you're working	you're working
he, she, it's working	they're working

EXERCISES

A. *Supply the present continuous form of the verbs in parentheses:*

1. John .... (do) his homework now. (John's doing his homework now.)
2. Look! It .... (snow).
3. I .... (read) *The New York Times.*
4. Mary .... (play) the piano now.
5. John .... (smoke) a cigarette now.
6. William .... (prepare) his lessons now.
7. I .... (read) a very good book at present.
8. Helen .... (write) on the blackboard.
9. We .... (speak) English now.
10. The teacher .... (talk) with Henry and Helen.
11. John .... (mail) that letter at this moment.
12. It .... (rain) hard.

B. *Supply the correct form of the verb in parentheses. Use the simple present tense or present continuous tense:*

1. John .... (come) here every day. (John comes here every day.)
2. John .... (come) here now.
3. Mr. Smith .... (smoke) very much.
4. Mr. Smith .... (smoke) a cigarette now.
5. John always .... (walk) to school.
6. John and Mary .... (walk) to school now.
7. The wind .... (blow) very hard now.
8. The wind .... (blow) very much in autumn.
9. Mary .... (play) the violin well.
10. Mary .... (play) the piano now.
11. The telephone .... (ring) now.
12. The telephone often .... (ring) during the day.
13. Look! That is John who .... (cross) the street!
14. Listen! Someone .... (knock) at the door.

C. *Change from simple to continuous form. In your answers make use of such expressions as* NOW, FOR THE PRESENT, FOR THE TIME BEING, AT THIS MOMENT*:*

1. John works here. (John is working here for the present.)
2. He reads *The New York Times* every morning.
3. She comes here every day.
4. He always sits in this seat.
5. He always gets on the bus at this time.
6. He eats in this restaurant every day.
7. The telephone rings very often.
8. He smokes very much.
9. He always walks to his office.
10. He teaches in this room.
11. He has an English lesson every day.
12. The train leaves on time every morning.

D. *Change from continuous to simple form. In your answers make use of such words as* USUALLY, OFTEN, ALWAYS, EVERY DAY:

1. He is studying hard. (He *always* studies hard.)
2. She is reading *The New York Times.*
3. He is working here.

4. He is sitting here.
5. He is smoking a cigar.
6. He is writing on the blackboard.
7. He is speaking English with the teacher.
8. He is talking with her.
9. I am studying English.
10. They are waiting for her.
11. He is playing the piano.
12. He is having a lesson.

E. *Complete the following in your own words. In your answers make use of such words as* NOW, EVERY DAY, ALWAYS *in order to make very clear the difference in meaning between the simple present and the present continuous tense forms:*

1. Helen is preparing .... (Helen is preparing her homework now.)
2. Helen prepares ....
3. We are studying ....
4. We study ....
5. Mr. and Mrs. Smith are traveling ....
6. Mr. and Mrs. Smith travel ....
7. Grace writes ....
8. Grace is writing ....
9. Mr. Reese is smoking ....
10. Mr. Reese smokes ....
11. William plays ....
12. William is playing ....

F. *Choose the correct form:*

1. The wind always (blows, is blowing) hard in this section of town. (The wind always blows hard in this section of town.)
2. John (prepares, is preparing) his homework now.
3. John told (to me, me) the story of the movie.
4. John (walks, is walking) to school every day.
5. We didn't hear the news and they didn't (also, either).
6. John is taller (as, than) any of us.
7. We didn't find (any, some) mistakes in the exercise.
8. No one (didn't come, came) to the door when we knocked.

9. Apparently, there wasn't (anyone, someone) at home.
10. They (have, are having) a big sale in Macy's department store today.
11. I (must, had to) work very late last night.
12. We (haven't to, don't have to) go to school on Saturdays.

G. *Answer these questions:*

1. What subject do you study every day at this time?
2. What subject are you studying now?
3. Does it rain often during the month of April?
4. Is it raining now?
5. What is your teacher doing now?
6. What are you doing now?
7. What is John doing now?
8. What kind of cigarettes does Mr. Smith smoke?
9. What kind of cigarette is Mr. Smith smoking now?
10. Is the sun shining now?
11. Who is knocking at the door?
12. At whom is William whistling?

LESSON 27

49. PRESENT CONTINUOUS TENSE—(Continued). The negative form of the present continuous tense is formed regularly; i.e., the negation *not* is placed after the auxiliary verb. The question form is also obtained regularly by placing the auxiliary verb before the subject.

John is reading the newspaper now.
John is *not* reading the newspaper now.
Is John reading the newspaper now?
What *is* John reading now?

50. PRESENT CONTINUOUS TENSE — IDIOMATIC USE. We often use the present continuous tense in English today as a substitute for the future tense.* In such cases an adverbial expression of time (*tomorrow, next week, Wednesday,* etc.) usually accompanies the verb and serves to indicate the exact point of future time.

John *is leaving* for Chicago *on Tuesday.*
They *are coming* to see us *tomorrow night.*

51. ARTICLES—(Continued). A special, idiomatic use of the indefinite article is shown in the following examples:

These gloves cost two dollars for each pair.
These gloves cost two dollars *a* pair.

The train travels at sixty miles per hour.
The train travels at sixty miles *an* hour.

EXERCISES

A. *Change to negative form:*

1. He's working hard now. (He isn't working hard now.)
2. It's raining.
3. John's preparing his homework.
4. The telephone's ringing.

---

*The attention of the student should be called to the fact that this use of the present continuous tense to show future time, although very common in present-day English, does not apply to all verbs; it is generally limited to a few special verbs of action or motion such as *go, come, leave, arrive, sail, fly,* etc.

5. Mr. Smith is teaching us today.
6. We're going to the movies.
7. John's writing a letter.
8. They're delivering the mail now.
9. He's leaving the building now.
10. She's eating in the cafeteria.
11. John's knocking at the door.
12. Helen's having her English lesson now.

B. *Change to question form. State each question twice, once in simple form and once with some interrogative word like* WHY, WHERE, WHAT, *etc.:*

1. It's snowing hard now. (a. Is it snowing hard now? b. How is it snowing now?)
2. Mary's reading her book.
3. The sun's shining.
4. John's swimming now.
5. They're sitting in the sun.
6. The teacher is writing on the blackboard.
7. The wind is blowing very hard.
8. The leaves are turning color.
9. The days are growing cool.
10. John's doing his best to learn English.
11. The weather's becoming warm.
12. Our lesson's beginning now.

C. *Change to present continuous tense:*

1. They will leave for Mexico on Wednesday. (They are leaving for Mexico on Wednesday.)
2. The boat will sail at two o'clock.
3. They will come to visit us sometime next week.
4. John will leave for New York early tomorrow morning.
5. We will go there tomorrow night.
6. He will fly to Chicago on Friday.
7. He won't get back until next week.
8. We will not leave before Wednesday.
9. Henry will bring several friends with him to the party tomorrow night.
10. We will arrive there Monday afternoon.

D. *Change the form of each italicized phrase to introduce the indefinite article:*

1. The meat cost sixty cents for *each pound.* (The meat cost sixty cents a pound.)
2. The eggs cost fifty cents *for each dozen.*
3. He comes here three times *each week.*
4. We have lessons four times *each week.*
5. We drove at sixty miles *each hour.*
6. The shoes cost five dollars *for each pair.*
7. He must take this medicine three times *each day.*
8. The bell rings twice *each day.*
9. He has to study at least four hours *each day.*
10. The teacher gives us an examination once *each month.*
11. I see him about twice *each year.*
12. The butter costs about fifty cents *for each pound.*

E. *Supply the correct preposition:*

1. Do you have any money .... you? (Do you have any money with you?)
2. Are there many pictures .... the wall .... your room?
3. John often writes letters .... the evening.
4. He puts the letter .... an envelope.
5. He prefers to write .... a pen.
6. The weather often changes .... the year.
7. It often rains .... the spring.
8. Do you often go .... the beach?
9. Do you like to lie .... the sun?
10. The leaves fall .... the trees .... the autumn.
11. John is writing .... the blackboard.
12. .... which season .... the year does it often snow?

F. *Choose the correct form:*

1. Look! Someone (comes, is coming) to call on us. (Look! Someone is coming to call on us.)
2. Our telephone often (rings, is ringing) during the day.
3. I didn't see (someone, anyone) in the room.
4. We didn't have (nothing, anything) to eat.
5. He sent (to her, her) the money.

6. (Was, were) John and Mary at the lesson yesterday?
7. John is (a, an) good English student.
8. John (said, told) me he could not come to the lesson.
9. (Have you, do you have) to go to school on Saturdays?
10. (Those, that) child seems to be sick.
11. The weather today is warmer (as, than) it was yesterday.
12. John is not so (big, bigger) as Henry.

G. *Answer these questions:*

1. What language are you studying now?
2. Who is that boy who is crossing the street?
3. Listen! Is the telephone ringing?
4. Does the telephone ring often or seldom during the day?
5. When is your friend leaving for Europe?
6. When is he coming back?
7. Is he going alone or is someone going with him?
8. Who is knocking at the door?
9. In what room is Helen having her English lesson?
10. In what room does she usually have her lesson?
11. Is it raining now or is the sun shining?
12. Does it often or seldom rain during the present month?

LESSON 28

52. *MANY-MUCH.* Many is used with things which can be counted or enumerated. *Much* is used with words of indefinite quantity or quality, with things which cannot be counted or enumerated.

> He reads *many* books.
> He drinks *many* cups of tea.
>
> He spends *much* of his time reading.
> He drinks too *much* coffee.

53. *FEW-LESS. Few,* like *many,* is used with things which can be counted or enumerated. *Less,* like *much,* is used with things which cannot be counted or enumerated.

> He has *few* friends.
> He drinks *fewer* cups of tea than I.
>
> He has *less* time than I.
> He drinks *less* tea than I.

54. *VERY-TOO.* Students sometimes confuse the use of *very* and *too. Very* means *much* or *in a large degree. Very* is used before an adjective or an adverb to make it stronger.

> He is *very* sick.
> She sings *very* well.

Too suggests something in excess, more of something than we need or can use. *Too,* when used with this meaning, is very often followed by an infinitive *(too* hot *to drink, too* difficult *to do, too* fast *to catch).*

> He is *too* sick to go to school today.
> The chair was *too* heavy for the child to lift.

EXERCISES

A. *Supply* MUCH *or* MANY:

1. John eats .... apples. (John eats many apples.)
2. Do you eat .... fruit?
3. Mary spends .... money on her clothes.
4. How .... times a week do you study English?
5. How .... time do you spend on your homework?

6. How .... coffee do you drink every day?
7. How .... cups of coffee do you drink every day?
8. He spoke to me about it .... times.
9. He spent .... time on that problem.
10. I read .... books.
11. Do you do .... reading?
12. How .... cigarettes do you smoke each day?

B. *Supply* LESS *or* FEW:

1. I eat .... meat than fish. (I eat less meat than fish.)
2. I have only a .... English books.
3. John has .... books than I.
4. John spends .... time on his English than I.
5. I saw her only a .... times.
6. He spoke to me for only a .... minutes.
7. I have .... money today than I had yesterday.
8. He brought a .... things with him.
9. He seems to be .... intelligent than she.
10. He was here a .... days ago.
11. He has only a .... friends.
12. He has .... friends than I.

C. *Supply* VERY *or* TOO, *whichever seems to make the meaning of the sentence clearer:*

1. I can't put this ring on my finger. It's .... small.
2. Miss Smith speaks .... fast, but I can understand her easily.
3. Mr. Jones speaks .... fast for me to understand him.
4. Some of these exercises are .... difficult, but I can do them if I try.
5. However, one of the exercises yesterday was .... difficult for me to understand.
6. Grace is still .... sick to go to work.
7. This soup is .... hot. Be careful when you eat it.
8. This coffee is .... hot to drink.
9. The weather today is .... cold, but if we dress warmly we can go out.
10. It is .... hot today to sit in the sun.

D. *Rewrite these sentences, using* Too:

1. This tea is so hot that I cannot drink it. (This tea is too hot for me to drink.)
2. He is so old that he cannot do hard work.
3. The dog was so weak that he could not stand up.
4. The hill is so steep that the car cannot climb it.
5. The stone was so heavy that I could not lift it.
6. The meat was so salty that nobody could eat it.
7. I was so excited that I could not think.
8. The bird was so young that it could not fly.
9. The weather was so bad that we could not play tennis.
10. She was so angry that she could not speak.

E. *Change these sentences, using* Very *instead of* Too:

1. The man was too angry to speak. (The man was very angry.)
2. The sky was too dark to take any pictures.
3. She was too excited to tell us about it.
4. The car was too expensive for him to buy.
5. It was too late at night to call her.
6. He was too weak to get out of bed.
7. He was too old to get married.
8. The problem was too difficult for him to do.
9. The turkey was too big to get into our oven.
10. Those oranges are too sour to eat.

F. *Supply the correct article* (A, An, *or* The) *where necessary:*

1. I always speak to .... teacher when I see him in .... morning. (I always speak to the teacher when I see him in the morning.)
2. .... sun is shining now.
3. John is .... very good student.
4. .... Hudson River lies west of .... New York City.
5. We missed you at .... lesson yesterday.
6. During .... year, ... weather changes very often.
7. ....United States, which is located on .... continent of .... North America, is one of .... largest countries in .... world.

8. .... Canada is part of .... British Commonwealth.
9. Where is .... capital of .... Mexico located?
10. Some of .... exercises in this book are easy.
11. We shall open our books to .... today's lesson.
12. I must buy .... new book.

G. *Choose the correct form:*

1. He smokes (many, much) cigarettes. (He smokes many cigarettes.)
2. He has (less, fewer) books than I.
3. She spends (much, many) time on her English.
4. John brought (to me, me) the letter.
5. John (is sitting, sits) in his seat every day.
6. Last night we all (must, had to) write a composition at home.
7. (These, those) books over there on the table are John's.
8. I didn't see (someone, anyone) in the office.
9. How many eyes (does, did) a man have?
10. John left (a, an) hour ago.
11. Mary (studies, is studying) her English lesson now.
12. John is much taller (as, than) I.

H. *Answer these questions:*

1. Do you have much money or little money with you?
2. How many cups of coffee do you drink every day?
3. Do you drink much coffee or little coffee?
4. Do you have more books or fewer books than John?
5. Do you spend much time or little time on your English?
6. How much time do you spend each night on your homework?
7. How many hours each night do you spend on your homework?
8. Do you read many or few books?
9. Do you have many or few friends in the school?
10. Do you read many magazine articles or few magazine articles?

LESSON 29

55. *MINE, YOURS, HERS,* etc. The possessive adjectives (my, your, his, her, our, their), when used alone as pronouns, have the following forms:

my—mine	her—hers
your—yours	our—ours
his—his	their—theirs

This book is *my* book.
This book is *mine.*

This room is *our* room.
This room is *ours.*

56. *NO–NOT.* Students sometimes confuse the use of *no* and *not. No* is an adjective and therefore always modifies a noun.

He has *no* money and *no* friends.

Not is an adverb and thus is the usual negative word to modify all verbs (Example: He does *not* speak English. She will *not* go with us.) Furthermore, since it is an adverb, *not* is used to modify the indefinite article, all numerals, and all such adjectives as *much, many, enough, any,* etc.

Not a student in the whole school likes her.
Not one person came to the meeting.
Not many people want to know about it.

57. *BETWEEN–AMONG.* Note that the preposition *between* is used only when referring to two persons or things. When referring to more than two persons or things, use *among.*

I sat *between* the two boys.
The three boys divided the money *among* themselves.

EXERCISES

A. *Substitute possessive pronouns for the italicized words:*

1. This book is *my book.* (This book is *mine.)*
2. This room is *her room.*
3. This office is *John's office.*
4. He took her book and left *my book.*
5. These newspapers are *their newspapers.*

6. These are *his cigarettes.*
7. That notebook is *Helen's notebook.*
8. This one is *my notebook.*
9. Is this pencil *your pencil?*
10. Is this coat *your coat* or *her coat?*
11. These seats are *our seats.*
12. This desk is the *teacher's desk.*

B. *Complete the following by adding the necessary possessive pronoun:*

1. I have a dog; the dog is .... (I have a dog; the dog is mine.)
2. John has a dog; the dog is ....
3. Helen has a cat; the cat is ....
4. You have a pen; the pen is ....
5. Mr. Jones has a new car; the car is ....
6. Mary has a new pen; the pen is ....
7. We have two English books; the English books are ....
8. Helen and Mary have two English books; the English books are ....
9. I have a dog and a cat; the dog and the cat are ....
10. You have a dog and a cat; the dog and the cat are ....

C. *Change to introduce the correct possessive pronouns:*

1. This hat belongs to her. (This hat is hers.)
2. These books belong to them.
3. Those seats belong to us.
4. To whom do these pencils belong?
5. To whom does this notebook belong?
6. This pack of cigarettes belongs to John.
7. It doesn't belong to me.
8. It doesn't belong to her either.
9. To whom does this newspaper belong?
10. It belongs to the teacher.
11. It doesn't belong to us.
12. Does it belong to you?

D. *Change to use the verb* TO BELONG *instead of the verb* TO BE:

1. This seat is hers. (This seat belongs to her.)

2. This pencil is mine.
3. It is not yours.
4. Whose seat is this?
5. It is William's.
6. It is not mine.
7. It is hers.
8. These magazines are ours.
9. Those tables are theirs.
10. Whose room is this?
11. It is ours.
12. It isn't theirs.

E. *Supply* NO *or* NOT:

1. There were .... chairs in the room. (There were no chairs in the room.)
2. She does .... speak the language well.
3. Yesterday was .... Saturday.
4. .... a person in the room recognized her.
5. He has .... time to study.
6. There was .... enough gas in the tank even to start the motor.
7. There were .... many people at the meeting.
8. She is .... a very good student.
9. He has .... friends in the school.
10. .... a single person offered to help us.
11. There are .... many students absent from class today.
12. There are .... students absent from class today.

F. *Supply the correct prepositions:*

1. Have you read the story .... the grasshopper and the ants? (Have you read the story about the grasshopper and the ants?)
2. It is always best to prepare .... the future.
3. It is better to stay .... home .... such fine weather.
4. We have nothing .... you.
5. John likes the grammar exercises best .... all.
6. William, ... the other hand, prefers the conversation exercises.

7. Do you come to school .... bus or .... taxi?
8. He put the letter .... an envelope.
9. What does John do .... a letter after he puts a stamp .... it?
10. John was absent .... class yesterday.
11. .... autumn the leaves drop .... the trees.
12. The United States is composed .... fifty states.

G. *Choose the correct form:*

1. The two boys divided the candy (between, among) them. (The two boys divided the candy between them.)
2. He sat (among, between) the two girls.
3. These seats are (our, ours).
4. These are (our, ours) seats.
5. Every day, I (get, am getting) up at the same time.
6. John smokes (many, much) cigarettes every day.
7. I didn't hear (anyone, someone) in the room.
8. The number of people (was, were) very large.
9. They didn't go and we didn't (either, also).
10. They told (me, to me) the bad news.
11. I (must, had to) study very late last night.
12. When will he (return, returns) from his trip?

H. *Answer these questions, using possessive pronouns whenever possible in your answers:*

1. Is this book yours or William's?
2. Is this Helen's pen or mine?
3. Whose notebook is this, yours or mine?
4. In whose room did you leave your hat?
5. Whose hats are those on the floor?
6. Are these seats ours or theirs?
7. Are these cigarettes yours or John's?
8. Whose umbrella is that in the corner?
9. Whose books are these on the desk?
10. Are these gloves yours or Mary's?
11. Is this newspaper his or yours?
12. Is this newspaper yours or the teacher's?

APPENDIX

SAMPLE CONJUGATIONS

Verb: *To Be*

Present Tense		*Present Perfect Tense*	
I am	we are	I have been	we have been
you are	you are	you have been	you have been
he, she, it is	they are	he has been	they have been

Past Tense		*Past Perfect Tense*	
I was	we were	I had been	we had been
you were	you were	you had been	you had been
he was	they were	he had been	they had been

Future Tense		*Future Perfect Tense*	
I will be	we will be	I will have been	we will have been
you will be	you will be	you will have been	you will have been
he will be	they will be	he will have been	they will have been

Verb: *To Work* (Simple Form)

Present Tense		*Present Perfect Tense*	
I work	we work	I have worked	we have worked
you work	you work	you have worked	you have worked
he, she, it works	they work	he has worked	they have worked

Past Tense		*Past Perfect Tense*	
I worked	we worked	I had worked	we had worked
you worked	you worked	you had worked	you had worked
he worked	they worked	he had worked	they had worked

Future Tense		*Future Perfect Tense*	
I will work	we will work	I will have worked	we will have worked
you will work	you will work	you will have worked	you will have worked
he will work	they will work	he will have worked	they will have worked

Verb: *To Work* (Continuous Form)

Present Tense

I am working	we are working
you are working	you are working
he, she, it is working	they are working

Past Tense

I was working	we were working
you were working	you were working
he was working	they were working

Future Tense

I will be working	we will be working
you will be working	you will be working
he will be working	they will be working

Present Perfect Tense

I have been working	we have been working
you have been working	you have been working
he has been working	they have been working

Past Perfect Tense

I had been working	we had been working
you had been working	you had been working
he had been working	they had been working

Future Perfect Tense

I will have been working	we will have been working
you will have been working	you will have been working
he will have been working	they will have been working

Verb: *To See* (Passive Voice)

Present Tense

I am seen	we are seen
you are seen	you are seen
he, she, it is seen	they are seen

Past Tense

I was seen	we were seen
you were seen	you were seen
he was seen	they were seen

Future Tense

I will be seen	we will be seen
you will be seen	you will be seen
he will be seen	they will be seen

Present Perfect Tense

I have been seen	we have been seen
you have been seen	you have been seen
he has been seen	they have been seen

Past Perfect Tense

I had been seen	we had been seen
you had been seen	you had been seen
he had been seen	they had been seen

Future Perfect Tense

I will have been seen	we will have been seen
you will have been seen	you will have been seen
he will have been seen	they will have been seen

SUBJUNCTIVE MODE

Verb: *To Be*

Present Tense

(If) I be	(If) we be
(If) you be	(If) you be
(If) he, she, it be	(If) they be

Past Tense

(If) I were	(If) we were
(If) you were	(If) you were
(If) he, she, it were	(If) they were

Other tenses are the same as those in the indicative mode.

PRINCIPAL PARTS OF COMMON IRREGULAR VERBS

Present	*Past*	*Past Participle*	*Present*	*Past*	*Past Participle*
arise	arose	arisen	eat	ate	eaten
awake	awoke	awakened	fall	fell	fallen
be	was	been	feed	fed	fed
bear	bore	born	feel	felt	felt
bear	bore	borne	fight	fought	fought
beat	beat	beaten	find	found	found
become	became	become	fling	flung	flung
begin	began	begun	fly	flew	flown
bend	bent	bent	forget	forgot	forgotten
bet	bet	bet	forgive	forgave	forgiven
bind	bound	bound	freeze	froze	frozen
bite	bit	bitten	get	got	gotten (got)
bleed	bled	bled	give	gave	given
blow	blew	blown	go	went	gone
bring	brought	brought	grind	ground	ground
build	built	built	grow	grew	grown
burst	burst	burst	hang	hung	hung
buy	bought	bought	have	had	had
cast	cast	cast	hear	heard	heard
catch	caught	caught	hide	hid	hidden
choose	chose	chosen	hit	hit	hit
cling	clung	clung	hold	held	held
come	came	come	hurt	hurt	hurt
cost	cost	cost	keep	kept	kept
creep	crept	crept	know	knew	known
cut	cut	cut	lay	laid	laid
dare	dared	dared	lead	led	led
deal	dealt	dealt	leave	left	left
dig	dug	dug	lend	lent	lent
do	did	done	let	let	let
draw	drew	drawn	lie	lay	lain
drink	drank	drunk	light	lit	lit
drive	drove	driven	lose	lost	lost

PRINCIPAL PARTS OF COMMON IRREGULAR VERBS—Continued

Present	*Past*	*Past Participle*	*Present*	*Past*	*Past Participle*
make	made	made	spend	spent	spent
mean	meant	meant	spin	spun	spun
meet	met	met	split	split	split
owe	owed	owed	spread	spread	spread
pay	paid	paid	spring	sprang	sprung
put	put	put	stand	stood	stood
quit	quit	quit	steal	stole	stolen
read	read	read	stick	stuck	stuck
ride	rode	ridden	sting	stung	stung
ring	rang	rung	strike	struck	struck
rise	rose	risen	string	strung	strung
run	ran	run	swear	swore	sworn
say	said	said	sweep	swept	swept
see	saw	seen	swim	swam	swum
seek	sought	sought	swing	swung	swung
sell	sold	sold	take	took	taken
send	sent	sent	teach	taught	taught
set	set	set	tear	tore	torn
shake	shook	shaken	tell	told	told
shine	shone	shone	think	thought	thought
shoot	shot	shot	throw	threw	thrown
show	showed	shown	understand	understood	understood
shrink	shrank	shrunk	wake	woke	woke
shut	shut	shut	wear	wore	worn
sing	sang	sung	weave	wove	woven
sink	sank	sunk	wed	wed	wed
sit	sat	sat	weep	wept	wept
sleep	slept	slept	wet	wet	wet
slide	slid	slid	win	won	won
slit	slit	slit	wind	wound	wound
speak	spoke	spoken	wring	wrung	wrung
speed	sped	sped	write	written	wrote